VIRGINIA HENDERSON
The First Ninety Years

VIRGINIA HENDERSON

The First Ninety Years

By

James P Smith OBE, BSc(Soc), DER, SRN, RNT, BTA
Certificate, FRCN, FRSH

SCUTARI PRESS

© Scutari Press 1989

A division of Scutari Projects, the publishing
company of the Royal College of Nursing

First published 1989

British Library Cataloguing in Publication Data

Smith, James P. (James Patrick), *1934–*
    Virginia Henderson: the first ninety years.
    1. Medicine. Nursing. Henderson, Virginia
    I. Title
    610.73′092′4

ISBN 1-871364-28-0

Cover photograph Jim McGinn/*Nursing Standard*

Typeset by MC Typeset Limited, Gillingham, Kent
Printed and bound in Great Britain by
St Edmundsbury Press, Bury St Edmunds

Contents

Contents

Foreword

This is one of the most important nursing books to be published for many decades. It contains the fascinating recollections of the world's greatest living nurse.

Virginia Henderson is known and loved in so many countries around the world for her clarity of thinking, her simplicity of approach and her deep and penetrating analysis of nurses and nursing.

Having retired more than 30 years ago, Virginia Henderson has spent her years in a very different way from her illustrious predecessor, Florence Nightingale. Whereas Nightingale chose to have the world come to her by staying in her house (some say actually in her bed!), Henderson has chosen to go to the world, and still accepts invitations to speak in several countries during the course of an average year.

I had the privilege to be the only foreign speaker at the celebrations for her ninetieth birthday in 1987 at Yale University in Connecticut. It was a thrilling and historic occasion and one that I wish the world's nurses could have shared. However, here we have an equal treasure in these recollections and reflections, which Jim Smith has so skilfully put down as a result of interviewing Virginia Henderson at great length in her home in Connecticut.

This book came about during the course of a discussion over dinner one evening at the Royal College of Nursing, where Virginia Henderson and Vernice Ferguson were the principal guests. Jim Smith was there, and we suddenly discovered that no book had been written about Virginia Henderson's life and times. I said to Virginia that the RCN and Scutari would love to be associated with this and would she agree to my seeking to raise funds for Jim Smith to visit her to undertake this work. She delighted us by agreeing immediately, and Vernice Ferguson instantly made a generous donation towards the project by writing a cheque there and then.

That was one of those magical evenings and this is a magical book. I hope that all nurses will read it, however old or young they are and whatever their perspective on the nursing profession. If their enthusiasms are flagging even slightly, Virginia Henderson's vibrant personality, charm and sense of humour will come through and make them proud to belong to a profession that harbours in its ranks such an outstanding and committed leader.

Trevor Clay MPhil RGN RMN FRCN
General Secretary of The Royal College of Nursing
of the United Kingdom (1982–89)

Preface

Virginia Avenell Henderson was born on 30 November 1897. I suppose it would be true to say that she was born into a dynasty — the Abbott dynasty. This large and extensive family was established on the marriage of Virginia's maternal grandparents: Lieutenant William Richardson Abbott (1839–1916) to Lucy Ridgeway Minor Abbott (1838–1921). Lieut. Abbott had served in the Confederate Army during the American Civil War. One of their daughters, Lucy Minor Abbott, married a Daniel Brocius Henderson, and Virginia Henderson was one of their eight children.

The roots of the Abbott dynasty, of which the Henderson family is an important part, are set firmly in Bedford County, in Virginia State, in the United States of America. In particular, in a large house there called 'Bellevue', which was formerly the Bellevue High School, and was once a thriving boys' school. In addition, there were four buildings that housed the students. Bellevue was actually founded by James P. Holkum in 1868. He was a former distinguished professor from the University of Virginia. He was an ardent secessionist, although his family did not believe in slavery; he was a spy for the Confederacy. Mr Holkum married an Anne Watts of Oakland in Roanoake County whose dowry contained a large number of slaves. Apparently Mr Holkum originally bought Bellevue mainly to house the slaves.

In 1870 Mr Holkum invited Virginia Henderson's grandfather to join the Bellevue Faculty as Associate Principal and instructor in Latin, Greek and English. The school had an interesting curriculum for its time, and classes were given in ancient and modern languages, commercial law, history, mathematics and the sciences. The school's reputation was built on academic excellence. Apparently, the students leaving the school were so good they were not required to take entrance examinations for the University of Virginia. Most of them had enough Latin and Greek to have a BA requirement before they even got to college, and many students went on to excel in both academic work and sport at the University of Virginia (affectionately known as 'The University').

Following the death of Mr Holkum in 1873, Mr Abbott became headmaster, and after that time he kept the student body to about fifty at any one time. 'Bellevue' as a school was closed down in 1909. Virginia Henderson's father taught at Bellevue and it was there that he met the Abbott's oldest daughter, Lucy, and married her. They moved to Kansas City after their marriage, where he practised law and was a specialist lawyer for the American Indians.

Daniel and Lucy Henderson had nine children but one died in infancy. The eight children who survived in order of seniority were Lucy Ridgeway, Charles, William Abbott, Jane, Virginia Avenell, Frances Minor, Daniel Brocius, and John Overton.

The history of the growth of the Abbott's dynasty was recorded by James P.C. Southall who married one of Virginia Henderson's aunts, her Aunt Jeannie, who was Virginia's mother's sister. His history of the family is called *Memoirs of the Abbotts of Old Bellevue*. It was published by the University of Virginia Press in 1955.

When the newly-married Hendersons moved to Kansas City in the late 1880s it was a boom town, but that did not last for very long, and James Southall suggests that the boom in Kansas City subsided 'the day little Virginia was born'. In 1901 the Henderson family decided to return to their roots in Bedford County and came back to live in one of the school houses near Bellevue. Virginia remained for a couple of years in Kansas City with her paternal Aunt Anne, and her father transferred his legal practice to Washington DC, where he lived most of the time, and came home from time to time to Bellevue to visit his family. James Southall records 'those little Henderson boys and girls fresh from Kansas City made quite an animated congregation, had some mighty cute tricks and ingratiating qualities . . . '. They appear to have brought a breath of fresh air to Bellevue.

In 1908 the Henderson family acquired a house of their own about a mile away from Bellevue. They called this house 'Trivium' and since that day this house has been a Henderson stronghold in Bedford County. Bellevue and Trivium were, therefore, two places where Virginia Henderson spent quite a lot of her early formative years, where she was educated, where she made her first friends and where she was part of a very happy extended family network. Grandfather was also a lay reader in the Episcopalian Church and held services every Sunday in the study at Bellevue. Her grandmother played the organ and apparently always rounded up enough family members and boys to have a choir. During the summer months the study became the family parlour.

Bellevue is still owned by the Henderson family, and Jane Henderson, Virginia's older sister, lives there and is a kind of curator of the Hendersons' roots.

When Virginia Henderson reached the age of ninety in 1987 it was decided about time that the details of her long and fascinating life should be recorded for posterity. The following pages are an attempt to do that.

The facts and information contained in this biography are the result of an analysis of several hours of conversation with Virginia Henderson and people who knew her well. These conversations were taped during the period 20 March to 10 April 1988 when the author had the delightful and uniquely memorable experience of being a guest in Virginia Henderson's home in New Haven, Connecticut, USA. During that happy time, both Virginia and her friend, Ruth Gardner, nearly killed him with kindness. This publication is dedicated to them both.

Finally, this biography would certainly never have appeared without the very great personal encouragement from Trevor Clay, former General Secretary of the Royal College of Nursing of the United Kingdom, and from Vernice Ferguson, deputy assistant medical director for nursing programmes, Veterans Administration, Washington DC, USA. I shall be eternally grateful to them both for their support.

James P Smith

CHAPTER 1

Early Days with a Large Family

Virginia Henderson was born in Kansas City, USA, in 1897. Her father had opened a law office because there was then a boom in Kansas City and it was thought to be a good opening for a young man. She was a middle child and feels sure that 'any psychologist will have a great deal to say about the effect of being the middle of eight children; I don't think I know enough about it to be a good judge on it.' Virginia has very few memories of Kansas City. She was between three and four when she left there. She can recall the way the front hall and steps looked, but that is all.

The Henderson family left Kansas City in 1901 and returned to Bedford County (Virginia). Virginia's mother had lived there all of her life except when she was sent to school to an aunt (Jenny) — her father's sister — who had a very small school in Georgetown just outside Washington DC. She spent several years there at Aunt Jenny's school but Virginia's mother's roots were very much at her childhood home — Bellevue.

Life at Bellevue was solitary but happy. It was the kind of life that almost excluded the rest of the world because it was so complete. The school always had visitors and parents visiting the school. Grandfather was a great whist player and there were always parties in the evening. People came from Pittsburgh and other cities with teams of boys to compete with teams from Bellevue in baseball games. 'The baseball field was right out in front of the big house and we all streamed out to watch the baseball game.' The teachers played in the teams as well as the boys, 'but we were all involved', Virginia recalls.

The Henderson children who were old enough went to grandfather's classes. It must have been quite an experience for the girls because it was a boys' school and boys were not used to seeing girls in their classes. Grandfather was a classics scholar. Everybody in the school took Latin and many of them took Greek as well. Grandfather did not think history was a proper subject to be taught in school because he thought that any intelligent and educated person would want to read it for pleasure. There was not too much attention paid to English grammar because grandfather believed that if you knew Latin grammar 'it followed on to English grammar'. He had a fine reputation for preparing people for university.

When the Henderson family moved to Bedford County, Virginia stayed with an aunt in Kansas City and joined her family later. She remembers

1

very well the culture shock of the family reunion and being suddenly thrown in with sisters and brothers. Her older sister made the comment that Virginia was very spoilt, having lived with adults for a year or more. 'She wrote to somebody and said I was very spoilt but she was working on me! I seem to remember that they did work on me. I think mother tried to soften the blow by having me sleep in a cot in her room for a while, or maybe there was not enough room in the nursery, or maybe she thought it would make it easier for me.' She was not yet old enough to go to school at Bellevue and was taught by a governess for a while, together with some cousins — the Wilson family. Their father had recently died and grandfather invited the widowed mother with her children to come to Bellevue.

Virginia remembers learning very little and finding the atmosphere rather uncongenial, which, she believes, may have prejudiced her against intellectual activities for the rest of her life — but she is not sure! She was taught reading, writing and arithmetic. 'In those times the people who were teaching you were very likely to be teaching you something they were interested in; and if you did not have the right answer you were very likely to be given a good whack.'

The Henderson family of eight children all had their own responsibilities within the house and household. This was the case even though Virginia recalls: 'When we were living in Bellevue there were very many people who we called servants — I don't know why — that word goes against the grain with me now. I suppose I have developed such an egalitarian attitude towards life that I don't like to think of one human being having to be at the mercy of another. I would never refer to anyone who works for me as "my servant".' The servants were black but there was no barrier between the whites and blacks. Great grandmother, for instance, had her particular servant. She would say things which were thought very funny; when they were going downstairs, grandmother would say: 'Now, Amanda, you go first, so if I fall, I'll fall on you.' It did not sound very kind but they both accepted it in the spirit of helplessness. Their cook was a lame black man who was considered an awfully good cook in his day. He was married. The first thing the family did when they came home was to go to his house because they loved him. He remained there until he died.

The kitchen was underneath the big dining room where, during the school session, both the students and the family dined. Virginia's mother had a special table in that very big room and there was a long table for the schoolboys.

As Virginia was fairly indisciplined and giggled a lot, grandfather used to threaten to spank her if she didn't stop. To the amazement of the other children she regularly told him he could but it wouldn't do any good. It delighted grandfather to be challenged like that even though he was very much a disciplinarian; but he was fair. Virginia's parents' discipline was firm but kind, expecting their children to do what was right.

2

After Kansas City, Virginia's father opened an office in Washington DC, coming home as often as he could, but he was an 'honoured visitor' when he came. Very little was done to disturb him — 'we wanted to make it so pleasant that he would stay. Father was a very gentle man.' He was absent for long periods. As he was a lawyer for the Indians, he had to go to their reservations over in the western part of the USA. He might be gone for months at a time. It was quite an heroic life because he had to learn all he could about how they lived and what their problems were. He had to learn to eat what they ate, for example, rattlesnake, because he was a guest. The Indians had great affection for him because they had special names for him. One of the names was 'Little Shingaben', which meant 'Little Fir Tree'. Father was a short man and Virginia thinks 'Little Fir Tree' was a very affectionate nickname. Virginia is short, too!

Virginia's mother had some education at Bellevue School at a time when education for women was uncommon. And Virginia claims that 'everybody in our family read all the time and talked about books and quoted poetry, and you couldn't help feeling that if they were not well-educated, they were cultivated people.'

There was a fine intellectual tradition from the maternal grandparents. Grandfather was unusually scholarly; there is no question about that. Grandmother was the daughter of a doctor and she grew up in an atmosphere of learning. She was also a very fine musician. It was said that when grandmother played 'Dixie', it sounded as if a whole band was at the piano instead of just one person. She taught music and supported herself by giving piano lessons before she and grandfather moved to Bellevue. Virginia's Uncle Frank had a way of saying, 'Now, children, I am going to ask you a question, and if you don't know the answer you don't belong in this family.' 'That very often made me realise that I didn't, because I very often didn't know the answer', Virginia contends. 'However, grandfather had a very large and excellent library and I think it is very much to his credit that he let us come in there and take any book we wanted to read. That didn't mean that he hadn't edited the contents of that library because I understand he kept some books locked up, to keep them away from his children.'

The dining room was very often cleared for games or dancing on Saturday nights. There was always some form of refreshment, either chocolate gummy caramel or maybe ice cream, or cakes or something to share with the boys. 'We had awfully nice parlour games, guessing games, charades. I remember those Saturday nights as wonderfully exciting because we were always in love with some handsome boy from the school.'

In the early years after coming back from Kansas City, the Hendersons lived in a small house attached to the school and then moved to another larger house. When Virginia was about ten or eleven her father and mother found a house about a mile away.

'It was an old house. Part of it had been an Inn and there was a well in the front yard. It had a mile long lane before you came to the main road, which meant that you could go three ways — and that is why grandfather gave it the Latin name of 'Trivium' — three ways. It was pretty uncomfortable until they pulled down the front part of the house, leaving four rooms at the back and a cellar. A lean-to was made into a kitchen, which was pulled down when we duplicated that part of the front of the house with the same size house at the back, giving us four bedrooms upstairs, one downstairs, a large living room, dining room, kitchen; and it became a very comfortable house. Later it was made especially comfortable for mother and father after his retirement. There was a porch on the other end to balance it, and it made a very attractive house.'

All the children had to do household chores then because they never had more than one servant and cook; but they enjoyed it. All the boys did a great deal of the outside work. The family considered it was so wonderful to have their own house and to have so much more space. There were 120 acres, a tennis court in the front yard, a garden in the back and a big vegetable garden. A cottage was built in the yard called the 'boys' cottage' and any number of boys seemed to be able to pile into that cottage. There were four rooms in it and upstairs could be turned into another dormitory. Mother was considered the most hospitable person in the world, and no matter who came to see her, or at what time of day, she would say, 'Oh, can't you stay the night?' She would sleep on a couch in order to be hospitable to anyone who wanted to stay. Lucy, Virginia's eldest sister, one day found that her room had been taken over by visitors. She protested to mother who replied, 'Oh Lucy, I have paid you the compliment of thinking you would be glad to give up your room.'

Charles, the eldest brother, because father was away from home, took on the role of a 'father' to the younger children. He disciplined the two little boys. Lucy was the eldest of the eight children, followed by Charles and Abbott who were absolutely devoted to each other. They couldn't get together for a minute without joking. Then came Jane and Frances and Virginia — called the 'three little girls'. Even their younger brothers always spoke of them as 'the three little girls'. Then the two younger brothers came, who were 'the little boys'. Charles was a great disciplinarian to the two little boys.

Charles was good at so many things; he helped the carpenter to build an addition to the house. He did not go to college until he was past the age when most people go because he wanted to help establish the family comfortably in that house. Just a year or two before he died he talked to Virginia about those years at Trivium and he said he wished he could live them all over again. He remembered them with so much pleasure. Charles, later in life, became Dean of the Engineering School at the University of Virginia, known as 'The University'.

Soon after the family went to Trivium, Uncle Willy died, and his two

4

older sons, William and John, were at loose ends and they and their mother — Aunt Lucy — came to live at Bellevue. The two boys went to a class that was set up by Virginia's Uncle Charles, and Virginia and her sister, Jane, were included. They had a very interesting curriculum consisting of Latin, history, mathematics, algebra and geometry. They were certainly encouraged to read widely from grandfather's library. As a very young child Virginia read Dickens and Thackeray and books of that sort and was critical of the younger children who read books that she thought were trashy! She had many an argument about it. 'I, of course, couldn't really compete with these two older boys and my sister, Jane, who was an excellent scholar', Virginia says, modestly, and recalls, 'I remember at that time hearing my Aunt Lucy, the mother of these two boys, asking Uncle Charley, "Who is smarter?" — Jane or me. Uncle Charley, to my amazement, said that "Virginia has as good a mind as Jane, but she doesn't know how to use it." That gave me some hope!'

Jane later went to Sweetbriar College and did extremely well there. Virginia remained with Uncle Charley who extended his class to include a group of neighbourhood boys. One of them was very, very bright, Virginia recalls, and they regularly exchanged notes on how many problems they had solved. She was determined to do as well as that boy (Herbert Thompson), who afterwards became a millionaire and joined the Coca Cola family.

Virginia was the only girl with about twelve boys. But later, when sister Jane came back home, she taught her two younger sisters (including Virginia) and two younger brothers. That was very traumatic for Virginia because she felt too close to Jane's age. Jane was home for a year before returning to finish her course at Sweetbriars. After Jane went back to Sweetbriars, Virginia returned to complete her high school education with Uncle Charlie. There was no formal award or any certificate; Virginia therefore did not 'graduate' from high school in the conventional sense.

The Henderson family were a very united family; everbody was interested in everybody else's welfare and unusually devoted to each other. They all helped each other. Certainly the family letters from that period show a great deal of affection and interest in each other. They laughed a lot. They felt the same things were funny. There were certain words, however, that put a person down in their estimation if they used them. For instance, you did not say things were 'cute', but 'splendid' and 'interesting'. But there was also a great deal of disagreement, albeit good-natured. They would sometimes sit up until two o'clock in the morning discussing what was 'charm'. Virginia says, 'We quarrelled day in and day out but the arguments were very interesting and there was a great deal of laughing all mixed up with it. There wasn't much animosity as far as I can remember. And, of course, there was rivalry.' A number of her brothers and sisters went on to college but Virginia didn't. She does not remember minding because she liked the things she was doing. She liked raking the leaves up and planting things in the garden. She also liked making curtains for the house.

Virginia also enjoyed sewing and made all her own clothes (as she still does) and made clothes for her mother and sisters. She liked acting. But she had many periods of gloom and doesn't know what triggered them off. She remembers her mother saying to her once, very sweetly, with no one else around: 'Virginia, if you could learn to control your moods you might be a fine woman some day.'

In those early days the only writing Virginia did was writing letters. Mother made the children write letters if anybody did anything for them. They had to write a 'thank you' letter regularly. It was just a socially accepted part of living to write letters at that time and they had to submit those letters, usually to some older person, for approval. Virginia never thought of herself as having any ability to write. In fact, when she went to Teacher's College years later and submitted papers to the English Professors — and was complimented — she was greatly surprised.

Virginia recalls, with sadness, her Uncle Jim (James Southall) coming back with the news that war had broken out in 1914. It was summer and he was staying at Bellevue. She can remember being terribly depressed by it: depressed even further with the US entry into the war and the knowledge that her older brothers and cousins were all of age to go to war. There were no pacificists in the family then. There was no question but that the boys were going to do what was expected of them. Virginia didn't have any of the violent anti-war opinions she now holds; she then didn't feel that they were transgressing any moral code by going to war. However, she now thinks it is stupid that we imprison a man for life when, in anger, he kills another man, and we pin medals on a man who goes and kills other men by the hundreds in war-time.

Virginia's brother, Charles, went overseas to war quite quickly. He had a pretty rough time but he was courageous about it. But he was very depressed after the First World War. Her other brother, Abbott, was training to be a pilot and he was with a group of pilots down in Texas being trained for overseas service. Transatlantic flights were not common in those days. In fact, aeroplanes were not built to cope with long flights. He was evidently a skilful pilot because he did a lot of flying at State functions: flying in formation. 'I think probably Abbott was scared to death the whole time because he never went in aeroplanes again. I think he had had his fill', Virginia believes. 'It was about this time I started thinking of becoming a nurse.'

6

CHAPTER 2

Starting to Train as a Nurse

It was the summer of 1918 when Virginia began writing to hospital schools. Her first applications were rejected! She then read about the Army School of Nursing, in Washington DC, founded by Miss Annie Warburton Goodrich, and that sounded very interesting to her. Her father went to see Miss Goodrich and persuaded her that although Virginia was a year younger than the age for entry (twenty-one), she had the potential to make a good nurse even without formal college education. Miss Goodrich accepted Virginia's application.

Virginia started in the autumn of 1918. The Armistice was declared soon afterwards. She remembers so well the excitement of the end of that war because the wealthy people in Washington DC opened their apartments and their houses to army nursing personnel, and they all watched the Victory Parade from elegant apartments. She can remember the excitement and the wonderful relief that the war was over at last. But in the spring of 1919 many of her fellow nursing students left and she lost many friends who decided that they did not wish to continue training as nurses. Nevertheless, Virginia completed her training with her two best friends, who later married two of her brothers).

It was a three-year training. The curriculum was made up of underlying sciences: biological sciences and some psychology, and social sciences; also anatomy, physiology, bacteriology, chemistry and some information about general health services. They had a preliminary nursing course consisting of the teaching of procedures with very little to hold the thing together. 'I don't think you would find nursing is taught like that today. I think it was a regrettable way really.' The preliminary course lasted about four months; then they began to go on the hospital units. They had able nursing instructors because Miss Goodrich could attract to that school some of the very best nurse educators for the time including a future editor of the *American Journal of Nursing* (Mary Roberts).

Students spent most of the day studying in those preliminary four months; Miss Goodrich made sure the days were not too long. The Army School was affiliated to a number of other nursing schools as they needed additional experience in a women's hospital, a children's hospital, in a psychiatric hospital, which was unusual in those days, and in public health nursing. Their days was limited to an eight-hour working day and they had

7

two days off a week, and an allowance of $30 a month: 'that was more money than I ever had in my purse and so I managed very well on it. It nearly killed me when we were told that we had to have outdoor uniforms made and I had to ask for $60 to get the uniform. I felt so bad about it.' Students also bought their own indoor uniforms.

Students had a month's vacation each year and had a very moderate working schedule. They were discouraged from working overtime even though Virginia often wanted to. 'For instance, one of the men I was interested in would be going to have an operation and coming back, and I wanted to stay with that man. If I could I would stay and hide and keep the head nurse from knowing I was still on duty.' Nursing students were part of the labour force but were not required to work unreasonable hours. Virginia functioned as a head nurse twice during her training period and once was responsible for the nursing on a thirty-bed ward. That was for a couple of months. Later when the supervisor in the operating theatre was sick for a week or two she took over those responsibilities.

After the four months of intensive study in the preliminary course, classes were then distributed so that they were held during the eight-hour working day. The three-year course ended with written examinations. They then became RNs in New York State. Some years later Virginia took the necessary examinations to register in the State of Virginia.

The New York standard must have been the highest, Virginia believes, because everybody wanted to be able to practise in New York State and wanted to be registered in New York State. It was considered a great thing for a nursing school in any other State to be examined by the New York examiners, and to be accredited, so that the graduates from that school could practise in New York State.

Miss Annie Goodrich, founder of the Army School of Nursing (and later foundation Dean of Yale University School of Nursing) had a profound influence on Virginia Henderson. 'Everybody was crazy about her and she had a way of treating us as if we were grown people.' But many of the instructors were condescending and were resented very much by the students, many of whom had had very adult experiences. One of Virginia's friends, for instance, was in law school — another one was studying exterior design — landscape architecture. It was very hard on them to take the kind of discipline that was handed out. All nursing schools at the time just didn't treat people as if they were mature, even though they gave the students tremendous responsibilities as nurses. Virginia cannot remember being sent to 'the office' very often, but once protested because one woman wasn't included in the group of patients who were being introduced to a European dignitary who was visiting the ward that day. Virginia was indignant because that patient was thoroughly looking forward to it and was very disappointed. 'I thought it was a terrible thing to do to her, but I protested to the wrong person.' Virginia was reprimanded and told it was none of her business. It made her realise that conformity was the order of the day, even though she had never been considered a conformist since those days!

Miss Goodrich, however, had a way of making the students feel that they were making a big contribution. She made them proud that they were in the Army School and made them feel that they were going to do great things. She made them feel that the role of the nurse in health care in the USA, or any country, was very important and that nursing took a life-time of study. Miss Goodrich said a great many things that stick in Virginia's mind as being so helpful. For instance, she once said: 'There is no such thing as a menial task. There is a menial attitude towards work and you can build up a lot of resentment having to do certain tasks.' She argued that people shouldn't be the leaders — but ideas should be.

There were some head nurses whom Virginia admired. Some she questioned; like the one who called her to the office and said she might make a good nurse one day if she learnt not to talk to the patients. Virginia thought that head nurse was on the wrong track. 'I was at that time on a very bad ward with only five patients on it and there was nothing to do after you got through giving the baths and making the beds and getting everything lined up, and it looked as golden and as frozen as anything could look. It was too clean. It was too orderly and there didn't seem to be anything wrong in talking to the patients, it seemed to be the only humane thing that you could do. It was lonesome for them, too. So that I questioned a great many of the people who were teaching me or who were in charge.' She recalls the influence of Major Muscovitch who was a doctor at Mount Sinai. He visited the ward where she was working one day — a ward where the men had incisions in their backs and tubes put in which were irrigated periodically. It was a pretty awful life for them but Virginia got so interested in those patients and thought they were wonderful people. She can still remember the names of the men. The major complimented her work: 'She has only been in training for four or five months and she is a first class surgical nurse.' That was terribly exciting and encouraging to Virginia. She has a vivid memory of the few people who praised her. It encouraged her to think that she had some promise. 'The people who were critical didn't persuade me that they were right and I was wrong', she argues.

The patients who had surgery in those days were very difficult to care for, but for Virginia Henderson it was one of the happiest experiences as a student. The empyema wards were in the main building and there was a big ward for the enlisted men and a small ward for the officers. She felt so sorry for them having to go around with tubes in their backs. They really couldn't do very much. The dressings were tedious and time-consuming but she really loved every minute of it. She seems to have had a very happy relationship with those patients. There was a man on that unit named

Powers, a great joker, and because Virginia was from the State of Virginia, he nicknamed her 'peanuts'. Virginia does not know why that informality was allowed. Often when she was due to go off duty at seven o'clock all of the men turned over for her to rub their backs, she recalls, and somebody timed her so that she wouldn't give one of them more time than another. She was devoted to those patients.

One of the patients was a young officer who was a very 'spoilt' man but he liked Virginia. He also had a tremendous amount of money. Nurses were allowed to go out with the officers. Thanks to that officer, later, at least once a week a large limousine was hired to take them both to the theatre. Virginia saw everything good that came to town. One day the head nurse came to visit and found Virginia in the office with a young enlisted man who was helping her to get the tubes ready for the next day. He should not have been there but Virginia could see no harm in it and she was awfully glad to have the help. She remembers that experience as vividly as anything. To her great sorrow she was sent, as punishment, to the diet kitchen, which none of the nurses liked, but, happily, she recalls that she was allowed to bake cakes for every one of those men with their names in icing on them. Many of them came and lined up in front of the building where they knew she would have to pass by to thank her for the cakes. It was quite an experience.

Following the preliminary period the students had lectures by physicians with relatively fewer lectures by nurse instructors. There was more synchronisation of the theory and the practice than most nursing students at that time were having, so when they were taking care of children they had lectures on paediatrics, and when taking care of psychiatric patients they had lectures relating to that, and some during public health nursing experience.

Virginia's public health nursing experience was in the West side of New York. That unit (Henry Street) was directed by a very able nurse and even the senior nurses of that branch would make visits and take the students with them. They demonstrated how they worked with families. Students were discouraged from eating anything in the patient's house but Virginia remembers being very much amused by a teaching supervisor who sat down and ate 'this terribly awful thing the patient set before us, including tea which looked much more like strong black coffee to me. It seemed like poison when I was drinking it, and when we came out she admitted that she saw no way of getting out of it without insulting the patient.' After the initial visits to homes with the supervisor, students visited alone. Virginia does not remember much teaching on the floor in paediatrics or in the care of women. Students learned by watching graduate nurses function.

In the women's hospital there was no such thing as 'rooming in' then. The babies were immediately put into a nursery after birth. Virginia remembers being one of two nurses in a nursery where there were thirty new-born infants and running all day long taking care of those infants, and trying to learn which infant belonged to which mother. It was a terrific strain. There was so much work that she missed lunch because she could not see any possibility of getting the work done in the time allowed. Most of the nursing was done by student nurses in that hospital. They had more help from graduate nurses in the Army Hospital because there were a great many graduate nurses in the military service. Once when she was in charge of a unit for servicemen she had little help as there were members of the staff who were sick. She had some help from a very able Medical Corps man, a sergeant and a very intelligent man, who, to her great distress, got sick before she got through that experience and she had to suffer seeing him treated by people she knew he didn't have much confidence in. He was suspected of having meningitis. He even resisted having a spinal tap.

At the women's hospital no head nurse attempted to teach the students. It seemed that every day they were running a race to get through the work. They did carry a tremendous amount of responsibility in caring for the patients, which was fairly uncomplicated. Whereas Virginia's recollection of that experience is not too good, she does remember it as just real hard work. She remembers, with fondness, one particular doctor at the women's hospital. He was an older man; he wore a fancy waistcoat with embroidered flowers and he was a great favourite with patients, and they talked to him. Virginia remembers his talking interminably with patients and once, when he had left the patients, said, 'You certainly are wonderful the way you listen to them for such a long time without showing any impatience.' He said, 'Don't worry, Miss Henderson, I charge by the word!' She also remembers two interns — one of them was extremely attractive and the other one, she thought, was a rascal. She recalls little about that period except that it was very hard work and because of that she was away from home for Christmas.

Virginia's paediatric experience was unusual because the hospital was on a ship. There was a hospital connected with it on land which the students never saw. That hospital functioned in the winter for patients and in the summer the patients were taken to the ship that was set up like a hospital ship. On the upper deck there was a sort of day hospital for the children who needed really more of a vacation outside the city. A number of the mothers came to take care of the children. Students weren't assigned to that deck at all. The middle deck was the one Virginia was assigned to. It was a unit devoted to infants who were in cribs all day long except when picked up. The mothers had no function on that floor. Virginia says it was probably the best care she saw given to anybody.

The ship hospital was perfectly beautifully run by a tall woman whose name was Miss Egan, and she taught students in her office. The head nurses on that floor were very good. Virginia thinks that they gave more instruction and supervision than any of the head nurses in the other hospitals. Each student was given three infants to take care of; the shift was worked from 7 am to 7 pm and when the senior nurse was off for her four hours the students had six babies. (Students were only allowed to work eight hours at a time.) The care given to those babies was exquisite.

One of the infants assigned to Virginia was a mentally defective baby and she never loved anything more than that baby; she says, 'I can see why a mentally defective child gets such a hold on mothers. They are so dependent that it just brings out all your protective instincts.' She recalls her indignation with the doctor who said he was going to tie that baby down if it didn't stop doing something that was making it difficult for all the people on the floor. Virginia had a real struggle with him to persuade him that it was no way to treat an infant. He was very young and, like the other interns, she doesn't remember him being too helpful in terms of paediatric care of infants.

Virginia suspects that the patients were children whom visiting nurses had identified as needing a period of relief from the poor care that they were getting at home. She can't recall any of the diseases that they had, except that she remembers the mentally defective child was a problem to feed. He was terribly dependent on her for everything. 'We just bathed and fed them and picked them up. We were made aware of the desirability of showing them affection and interest. We were never limited to the amount of cuddling we could give the children. We were encouraged to handle them. Another thing we were held accountable for was keeping those infants warm. Miss Egan, when she made her rounds, felt the feet of all the infants to see that they were warm. We were scared to death when she found one had cold feet; that was an indication that we were not giving them the right kind of care.'

They were all very small infants. Parents never visited. Compared with present day experience in paediatric nursing, it was a very limited experience. Virginia concedes that most of what she learnt about the care of children was self-taught, even though some of the doctors gave lectures. Textbooks in paediatric nursing, like most books of that period, consisted of a series of descriptions of procedures. There was very little about the philosophy of nursing — a philosophy of what you should do for sick children or what you did for people of any age, or chronically ill or acutely ill people. No distinctions were seen clearly in nursing at that time. The only philosophy to be learned was from the way the students saw head nurses function in relation to the patients. The teaching of medicine and nursing then was extremely different from the teaching there is now. Virginia doesn't think doctors had a too well-defined philosophy either. Many of the doctors that she worked with had a remarkable bedside manner, nonetheless.

In Virginia's training days, students had experience with communicable disease 'everywhere' but special instruction was tied up with the experience at the Army Hospital, because there were plenty of communicable diseases in the hospital to provide good experience. She suspects that she had the best medical lectures on communicable diseases possible at that time.

One disease that the students had good instruction in was venereal disease — particuarly syphilis — and Salvarsan was used then with fairly good results. They were so aware of the different stages of syphilis; for example, in her early student days one of her patients for some reason resisted her giving him a bath, and she was equally insistent that he would oblige. When she turned him over to rub his back, the reason he didn't want her to bath him was because he was covered with pustules. Her instruction helped her to recognise them as the second stage of syphilis and she was very careful. She asked the head nurse to come and see if she was right. He was later transferred to the unit where syphilitic patients were treated. Virginia remembers feeling terribly sorry for him but also felt that she had been exposed to some danger without knowing what was wrong with the patient. That patient was nursed by Virginia during her first Christmas away from home.

Later, in the first year, she was assigned to a communicable disease unit in which gown and glove technique was taught very carefully. There were no cross-infections to her knowledge. It must have been pretty well done because she can remember taking care of patients with various diagnoses, including scarlet fever and measles. Many of the patients were quite young. They were nursed in long huts in which thirty patients were taken care of; each was divided into small sections so that patients with different diseases were not put together in the same room. During this period her sister, who was taking a secretarial course in Washington, got sick with a communicable disease, either measles or scarlet fever. Remarkably, Virginia was permitted to take an ambulance and get her and bring her back to the hospital where she stayed for several weeks until she was considered fit. 'We had a lovely time because everybody was terribly nice to us', Virginia recalls.

Patients with communicable diseases were kept in hospital much longer than they are now. There was no chemotherapy treatment; sulphonamides had not been developed. They did have immunising techniques at that time for certain communicable conditions but there were no antibiotics. Nursing care was really the only treatment, except for syphilis, which Virginia feels was very effectively treated.

The treatment of pneumonia was very poor. Sadly, Virginia recalls one experience when she didn't recognise the symptoms of a *crisis*. She thought that the patient was better because the temperature had fallen but actually the patient was in crisis and later died. 'This was when I was doing visiting nursing and I always wondered if I had missed the boat with that patient. It was one of the episodes of guilt that I experienced in feeling that I wasn't adequate.' As a student nurse, Virginia felt that she had not been adequately prepared to recognise that when the temperature suddenly drops in a patient with pneumonia, it is dangerous.

Virginia herself had viral pneumonia as a student, caught during a 'flu epidemic. It must have been a fairly bad case because she was kept in hospital for at least a month by a doctor who she thought was unnecessarily protective of her. He was very much afraid that she was going to have some complications. He was afraid that it had affected her heart, but, fortunately, it didn't.

As there was no chemotherapy in those days, febrile patients often had to be sponged. 'You would sponge the arms and legs and back and more or less let the body evaporate the water. The highest temperature I remember was, I think, 107°. We would reduce it to something like 102° or 103°. The patients found it agreeable to them — I expect it felt good.' In spite of some high temperatures, Virginia cannot remember a single death on the communicable disease unit. 'Certainly none of my patients died whilst I was taking care of them', she says.

Nurses didn't do anything for patients suffering from communicable diseases without wearing a gown: gloves were only used if there was a dressing or some lesion. Virginia is interested to see that dentists now put on gloves because of the present AIDS scare. In her day 'there was none of that hysterical protection. I wasn't afraid of taking care of people with my bare hands. We used the gloves to protect their wounds', she says. Masks were also worn.

For disinfection, Virginia is sorry to say that boiling was used with much more confidence then than later. She later challenged this at Columbia University around 1929 when she carried out a bacteriological study on the relative effectiveness of steam under pressure — and boiling — for surgical instruments. Her Master's dissertation was called 'Medical and Surgical Asepsis'. She got a great deal of help from Johnson & Johnson who then sold sterile supplies. A pathologist and bacteriologist helped Virginia to set up this experiment. At the time, she did a survey of the sanitary codes in the various States, making a comparison of what communicable techniques were required by the sanitary codes. They differed from State to State. She was really trying to promote steam under pressure for sterilisation and the abandonment of boiling. She was a tireless scientist and used animals for that experiment. It meant that she couldn't go anywhere or do anything because she had to feed those animals. She hated using the rabbits her supervisor insisted on to get spores to grow so that she could prove that she had destroyed them. Both her supervisor and Virginia were so dissatisfied with the incompleteness of the laboratory work that she eliminated any report of this in the dissertation because what she considered really useful was the comparison made of practices demanded by the sanitary codes. Virginia believes that her work demonstrated that steam under pressure was more effective than boiling.

Virginia's experience as a student in communicable diseases had a long-lasting impact on her. She was always searching for something that really seemed to benefit the human race. 'I want some assurance that what I am doing has value. I think that as a student nurse I could see the definite value in what I was doing to help that person get well from the disease, and protect other people. It was so obvious, it was so satisfying for me, so I wanted to see it used more universally and more effectively to help patients. Like Miss Nightingale, I have shared an interest in seeing the environment made safer for people. She put more emphasis on fresh air than I of course did. I had more opportunity to learn how to control bacterial infection than she did. To this day I want to see people very much more involved and careful about the spread of disease.'

Virginia thinks hospitals were safer in her student days because antibiotics have given modern day nurses a false sense of the importance of controlling disease with antibiotics, making doctors, nurses and everybody else careless.

Miss Goodrich saw things in a much larger framework than the people of her era — or possibly any era. She saw psychiatry as desirable, if not an essential, feature of the generic preparation of the nurse. All Army School of Nursing students were exposed to psychiatric care, which in those days was not too good by today's standards. Chemotherapy was used for some psychiatrically disturbed patients but was not too common. They relied a lot on hydrotherapy, which meant the nurse's role was quite intolerable because the hydrotherapy was given by both physiotherapists and nurses.

Virginia's psychiatric experience was taken with students that she didn't know; they could not ask to go with any special friends on any affiliation. She supposes they thought it was very narrowing to be thrown with the same friends all the time. The psychiatric hospital was called 'Bloomingdale'. It is still operating and when Virginia went to see a patient there fifteen or twenty years ago she was met by a nurse whom she recognised as someone who had been a student of the psychiatric nursing programme in Virginia's days as a student there. She had not liked this nurse or her treatment of patients but had envied her assurance and lack of fear in dealing with aggressive psychiatric patients. The nurse said, 'I don't think that you will find that there has been very much change.' Virginia concedes she didn't.

During her student psychiatric experience, Virginia did not learn very much about psychiatry or become convinced that what they were doing to people was particularly helpful, because too many of those people had been there for years and seemed to her to be fated to spend the rest of their lives in the institution. Students had classes with the psychiatric nurse-teachers there but 'they seemed to be so rooted in their teaching and in their behaviour, and looked to me as if they had never sat down in their starched white uniform. They were the most turned out people that I had ever seen

15

in their uniforms. I never felt as if I got to know them as human beings, although the two women who were in charge of the hospital nursing were entirely different kinds of women.'

Virginia's first assignment was on a unit for very disturbed patients who were in rooms with the doors locked, stark naked and talking gibberish. She remembers vividly a conversation with a woman who was a minister's wife and part of her gibberish was 'pop shits is up and up sticks is my name, and this is my shitting nurse'. The yelling coming from this minister's wife was so absolutely horrifying to Virginia that it coloured her experience — unnecessarily — she thinks because it seemed that something better could have been done for this woman than to lock her up in a room with no handle on the door on the inside. There was nothing in the woman's room but a mattress with a rubber cover on it. The room had to be mopped up two or three times a day. She was on Virginia's conscience all the time — her and others like her. That disturbed ward was just one horrifying experience to Virginia because all the patients were isolated that way in those rooms. To Virginia's consternation she had day duty experience there and then night duty. She was assigned to the short end of the ward as a night nurse and sat at a table in the hall 'with all these horrible sounds coming from the patients in the rooms . . . ' One woman, terribly disturbed with an anxiety neurosis, said continually, all night, 'I haven't got a cent, I haven't a penny even.' So every night Virginia decided to resign from nursing because she couldn't cope with this. She didn't feel she was doing anything constructive for them and didn't see that anyone else was. 'It was just one horrible nightmare to me', she says. Fortunately, Virginia didn't resign.

After that experience she was moved to a unit where the patients were less disturbed and she was even allowed to take some of them out for a walk. The more disturbed patients were only allowed to exercise in certain courtyards. When Virginia could take the patients out for a walk it was very much more gratifying for her but she never felt that she developed any adequate competency in dealing with psychiatric patients. 'I left that place feeling that we were very much in the dark ages with treating them. It was a kind of scary place to be anyway. It was up on the top of a hill. I remember that my Uncle Jim was very near and telephoned and asked me to come to New York because of my aunt's illness. I remember walking down that hill at night. It was about a quarter of a mile to the elevated train which took me into New York alone, and I think it was about as scary as anything I will ever do.'

Another vivid recollection of Virginia's is the importance of the phy-siotherapy department. One of the things they did was to make the students undergo all the therapeutic treatments that they gave patients. Virginia thinks that was good and thought the physiotherapists were wonderful. They put people in continuous tubs and Virginia believes those treatments were welcomed by the patients. 'I think the physical contact with another human being was welcomed. I think the treatments were soothing. I think it was a pity that we replaced that treatment with chemicals which turn these patients into zombies.' Bad as the overall treatment was, Virginia doesn't think it was much worse than now where the patients are, in her view, often just sitting around, tranquillised with chemicals and looking like a lot of zombies, unresponsive to attempted conversation.

Virginia never remembers psychiatric patients ever being discharged. She didn't see them getting well and going home. Many of them seemed to be hopelessly ill although the nurses were led to have confidence that the treatment was going to be effective.

There were occupational therapy programmes and Virginia remembers going to one dance where some patients were considered fit to participate in barn dancing with the nurses.

There was no such thing as the 'screaming room' for nurses that they now have in some of the hospices, that allow nurses to go and blow off steam. 'I suppose we must have had some support from the psychiatric nurses who were accustomed to this, I would rather say hardened to it, who seemed to be able to cope. I literally did not feel able to cope.'

At one time Virginia was placed on a unit where a woman from a prominent family was being cared for. She was a great big woman and she was given the run of the unit — a ward that did not have locked doors. Virginia was assigned as a sort of special nurse to this woman and was told that the last person who had taken care of the woman had been caught by her behind a door and she had smashed her very badly by pushing the door against her. Virginia was literally terrified of this woman but she developed her own way of dealing with the situation which she is sure was totally untherapeutic! Virginia decided that as this woman had come from 'the upper crust' and had been used to bossing other people and being treated with great deference, she would keep the woman happy by making her feel that Virginia would do anything in the world that the patient wanted her to do. Virginia would say to her therefore: 'Wouldst the queen have her hair brushed?' And she would reply 'Wouldst.' Virginia recalls that the patient 'would sit down and I would have a lovely time combing her hair, and because I was her handmaiden it suited her down to the ground, and it suited me down to the ground. That is an example of how little help we asked for or got in the treatment of people with particular problems.'

Virginia's experiences almost put her off psychiatric nursing for life. She is particularly scathing of the psychiatric nurse tutors who never appeared in the patient areas.

The most constructive thing the students saw was what the occupational therapists and physiotherapists did. Virginia is sure, to this day, that they are the most effective people in psychiatric health care. As far as she can see, they do people no harm and they do a lot of people a lot of good. 'Certainly the medical care we see is sometimes dubious, and certainly the nursing is sometimes dubious', she thinks. So far as she knows no student from the Army School who went to Bloomingdale was ever subsequently attracted to a career in psychiatric nursing.

Virginia's antipathy and ambivalence about psychiatric nurses and nursing did not mellow until the 1960s. Then she met an outstanding American psychiatric nurse, Ida Orlando. Ida Orlando's innovative work in psychiatric nursing at Yale University resulted in her developing the 'nursing process'. In 1961, Ida Orlanda wrote about her work in the book *The Dynamic Nurse–Patient Conflict*, which was published by Putnam.

Virginia now feels strongly that every nurse ought to have a general preparation before experience in psychiatric nursing because it is her conviction that so much of mental health depends upon physical welfare. She believes that unless you have respect for a person's physical needs, you have a pretty poor chance of helping them with the mental health problems. 'I know,' she says, 'when I am in my disturbed periods I don't sleep well. I don't eat well, and I get indigestion. I think it is problematical as to whether helping me to sleep and helping me to have normal digestion isn't a bigger problem in getting me over that psychotic episode I am in, than somebody trying to ferret out what is bothering me. Anyway, I will take my chances with the person who is interested in my physical well-being.'

Virginia Henderson still holds strongly that physical, mental and emotional care merges, and refuses in her writings to separate the emotional and mental care from the physical care. She has tried to merge them into any aspect of nursing. So she was delighted at Yale when she met Ida Orlando, working with a substantial grant to try to see how nurses in a generic programme could learn to practise nursing so that the psychic and emotional content of care was given as much recognition and emphasis as the physical. Their works complement one another. Virginia believes that Ida Orlando's concept is close to her own definition of nursing.

CHAPTER 3

Community and Social Relationships in the Army School

Virginia's three months as a student in public health nursing were, she says, wonderfully enjoyable. 'It was a perfectly delightful period of my life really because I was so much in accord with what I saw being done for human beings professionally, and because it was very unusually nicely arranged where I was to live whilst we were doing it.' Fortunately, she shared the experience with her two special friends who afterwards married two of her brothers. They were dear friends who together shared an apartment that belonged to a librarian who was on leave that summer. They cooked their own meals and, very conveniently, Virginia's brother, Charles, was living two or three blocks away with two men friends of his. They very soon made an arrangement that the six of them would cook dinner together. Two and two! One man and one woman would cook dinner on Monday night and so on. They were great friends and it was very congenial; they did many things together.

The work in public health nursing was particularly interesting because they had theory at Teacher's College, Columbia University. Miss Goodrich taught there and introduced them to all kinds of interesting people. The resources of Teacher's College were drawn on to make theory just about as rich as it could have been at that time. 'I don't suppose that there was anywhere that you could have gone in the country where knowledge of what community and public health nursing might contribute. I doubt if you could have found a richer interpretation of it as right there.'

The students felt they were really treated like intelligent adults. They were assigned to different offices in New York. The part that Virginia was in was called 'Hell's Kitchen'. Crime was rife in that area; there was certainly a lot of poverty; it was an Italian district. There were other groups, too, like the Irish, who always wanted to give the nurse very strong tea, which Virginia always turned down.

Virginia believes the students were very much more helped by the graduate nurse staff in learning how to function than in any other clinical situation. They went with the graduate nurse to see her functioning at first. The teaching supervisor in charge of that particular geographical unit often took the responsibility of going at least once with them and talking about

19

her ideas, and demonstrating how she would handle questions that arose in connection with the care of these people. Virginia no longer had the feeling of just being on her own without anybody to turn to. It was just excellent, she says. They met some of the great names in nursing.

She remembers being tremendously impressed with the recreational programme down at the Henry Street Settlement for the inhabitants of that region of New York. Virginia recalls the dances on top of the roof. Henry Street Settlement at that time was so famous and had such an influence on the life of New Yorkers, because Vivien Ward, who had started it, had really been responsible for introducing health care in the schools. She was respected all over that city, and feared by anybody who had any money, because she had a way of getting it away from them to contribute to the welfare of the city.

It was very wonderful, Virginia recalls, to see what that beautiful settlement house had done for the people in that community because one famous man after another was saying that he had got his start through what the people at that settlement had done for his family and himself, and how it had changed his life. It was exciting for the student nurses. They had all kinds of classes for new citizens who did not speak English, including, of course, classes in English. They had a curriculum that changed from year to year according to what the people needed. They had a recreational programme, a health teaching programme and speech classes. It was almost limitless the things that they gradually took on, including classes in dancing.

Visits were made to many people in their own homes. Virginia's own words record these vividly:

'We had a full day's work really with our bag in our hands taking care of patients. There were newborn infants who had been born at home and we took care of the infant and the mother. There was terrible poverty and I can remember the fear we all had that we would bring home bedbugs in our equipment or on our bodies because you would turn over a mother, or put a blanket over her, and you would just see bugs run for cover. You couldn't understand how she could tolerate the misery of that; but you saw the depths of poverty in that region and you also saw some pretty corrupt things. For instance, I remember a couple who I afterwards saw on the street — they looked like two very corrupt individuals. The mother was very swollen but the baby was not in sight and it mysteriously died; and I never did know what had happened to that baby. I remember that there was no food in the house. I remember buying the making of a meal and coming back and cooking a meal for them, because he was sick, too. He had ulcerated ankles. Oh, he was miserable and she was pathetic. But I met them on the street later and their faces were all painted up. I don't know who they were. They were miserable characters. I think they had something to do with trying to get on the stage. Nothing about them seemed genuine to me but I was very troubled with them not having enough to eat. I don't remember how we worked on that problem. There was no lack of people with whom I could talk about problems. As a student, in my experience, I could always put the burden of doing something about it on them. They never seemed to be unwilling to accept the burden of trying to do something to help people, using a non-judgemental approach to human misery, which I admired tremendously.'

Virginia recalls another family in which a little girl was sick and the grandmother was very prominent in the care of the child.

'She told me that the child was going to die but she asked me if I would like her to tell my fortune. I demurred because I never believed in that sort of thing. She insisted and, as so very often happens, they fix some tea for you, and you were told not to participate, but you couldn't for the life of you think of any humane way to say "I will not drink this tea with you" or throw it in the sink. So I sat there with this grandmother while she told my fortune by looking at my hand.' She told Virginia some very remarkable things. 'First place, she said, "I see a ship and I see somebody kin to you in connection with that ship and I think you are going to see him tonight." I thought it was perfect foolishness. Another thing she said was "I see you when you go home, but I don't know why I see it, but there is a well in your front yard. Is that true?" I had to admit it was because we had bought a place that had been an inn and there was a well in the front yard for a very good reason. She told me a lot of other things. She said, "As soon as you get home you will want to go somewhere else because somebody has been sick down there that you are very fond of." That was my Aunt Lily who was very ill. Any rate I went back to my apartment and that night I went over to my aunt's where I found my uncle who was heading for Europe on the boat. One of the things that grandmother had said about it — which was almost unbelievable — was "I don't see this man looking like most men. He is very dramatically dressed, I see him in a cape." Well, I'm darned if Uncle Frank didn't have a cape! That household made a big impression on me because, of course, I got very fond of the little girl and it was so painful to see her die.'

Another family Virginia remembers very vividly was one in which a child had been told it had to have treatment because it had lice in its scalp and she gave this child a shampoo over the kitchen sink. The father came in — it was an Italian family — and he was sympathetic to the child who was resisting this treatment. Virginia said to the father, 'Well, she has got little lice in her hair and they have got to be taken out.' The father said, 'Ah, little girl, she has a nice place for lice!' Virginia has never forgotten that father.

The mothers, children and newborn infants made up a large element of the public health work. They had very good classes for the pregnant women and there seemed to be a good rapport between the patients and nurses. That is why Virginia liked it so much better than hospital nursing because she felt hospital patients, to some extent, were nurses' victims. They had to accept what nurses did. The people on the district did not.

There was comparatively little, and practically no organised, teaching about death during her training, except that the students were taught what to do when the person died and how to prepare the body for the undertaker.

21

But the 'hospice philosophy' was completely lacking and this idea of keeping the quality of life good up until the last moment, if possible, was certainly not instilled in them. If patients in the Army Hospital were dying, screens were just put around them: 'I think that the students must have been protected from taking care of these patients because I don't remember any assignment for the care of the dying patient', Virginia recalls. Virginia thinks they must have been shielded for she also does not remember any experience in the emergency room where they might have seen a dying patient. The lack of teaching about death was, in Virginia's view, a great disadvantage and a great limitation.

Virginia thinks that having been a student nurse in the Army School of Nursing had certain unique qualities. One was that American nurses, during the First World War, came the nearest they have ever come to feeling that the public considered them superior, rather than inferior, by virtue of their being in nursing. The most distinguished, eminent, and often wealthy people went into nursing as a means of contributing towards human welfare, which was at risk during the First World War. There was great fear of that conflict lasting almost indefinitely, and people were grateful to those who adopted the nursing profession.

In the Army School of Nursing students met some of the richest people. For instance, there was nobody perhaps better off financially than the people who made the Kelly Springfield tyre for automobiles, and the advertisements for these tyres were on top of buildings and on the roadside and everywhere. It was a black tyre and through the tyre (in the adverts) was the head of this beautiful girl with red hair. That girl was the daughter of the Kelly Springfield family. 'I don't know why she allowed herself to pose in this position, but she was in the Army School of Nursing.' She was a fascinating person, Virginia recalls. 'She was beautiful, she was witty, she had of course had every possible social advantage, and she came with uniforms that looked as if they had been made by a couturier. They were ostensibly the same as the other students' uniforms, but everything about them was better.' Martha Kelly was one of the people who elected to leave the school when students were all told after the Armistice: 'Now decide whether you are going to finish the three-year programme of whether you are going to leave; we don't want you just to ooze out, we want you to declare your intentions, and if you are going to get out before the three years are up, do it now.' Martha decided to go but, to Virginia's delight, Martha gave her uniform to Virginia. She had never been better dressed in her life, she claims.

The daughter of the Senator for New York State was a nursing student also. She was beautiful, accomplished and fortunate in every respect. She left, but didn't give any uniform to Virginia! She was a loss because she had so much charm and beauty and everything else. Both of these two 'best friends' were people who had had advantages that Virginia hadn't had, and had been educated in private schools in France and Switzerland, had the most elegant manners, beautiful clothes and were very sophisticated in their approach to life compared with Virginia. Another very good friend of Virginia's had been educated in private school and had a year or two at one of America's most exclusive colleges for women.

Many other students in that school came from very fortunate families. Knowing them and their families gave Virginia a feeling of having enlarged her experience a good deal, because she had lived in the South all her life and most of her friends and associates had been Southerners.

As a result of the experience in the Army School of Nursing, Virginia came to have a feeling that nurses were accepted as important members of society and she believes she learned to take more of a fearless approach to health care, irrespective of 'the social status of the providers, whether they were doctors, nurses, physiotherapists, social service workers or whatso-ever'.

This early fearless approach is illustrated by the way Virginia coped with a difficult doctor in her student days.

> 'I remember, for example, as a student when I was in charge of the ENT unit. There was an ENT doctor who had a habit of cursing and swearing freely in front of us and I remember asking him if he would mind going somewhere and having a little private conversation with me, when I told him that that wouldn't do as far as I was concerned. I had the potential status of an officer and the patients and the poor men who worked with me were supposed to treat me with a certain amount of respect. Any rate, I expected it from the men that I associated with that their conversation would not make me feel as if they were disregarding my respectability, and I felt degraded by the way he talked. He was extremely apologetic and changed immediately and was always extremely nice to me. I think I wouldn't have taken this spurious approach if I hadn't felt that all around me nursing had a social acceptance and status, that perhaps some nurses have not enjoyed to the extent that we did.'

Virginia believes she lost her identity as a Southerner more or less as the result of being in the Army School of Nursing and living in Washington DC, where there was a very cosmopolitan population. Her fearless approach socially to the problems of nursing, she believes, was influenced particularly by the positive public image of the nurse which has since, she argues, diminished in the USA. The public does not have the image of the nurse as a professional worker with a large intellectual component now, in her view, but rather as a pair of hands to do somebody else's bidding. In the Army School they had a very different feeling about nursing, from Miss Goodrich in particular. If anybody tried to treat them badly, they learnt to stand up for their position. But Virginia admits that the ethos at the Army School was unique for when she was having experience at the women's hospital in Washington she noted a difference in the way nurses were treated there. When she did visiting nursing in New York City among impoverished immigrants, they had an exalted view of the importance of nurses.

She experienced a range of reactions to nurses and nursing which showed a range of public images of the nurse. It was a good thing, she believes, that her experience enabled her to sample this range. Virginia applied these insights at the psychiatric hospital, for example, with the psychopathic woman from the upper classes who enjoyed being treated so that she could then behave condescendingly to Virginia. That made the patient feel natural but, Virginia concedes, 'I did it for self-protection. I did it on purpose. I used what I saw as her image of a nurse as a means of protecting myself.'

The attitude of doctors to nurses in the Army School of Nursing was probably different and better than in most places as they were working on a salary. They weren't 'fee for service' people. They were not so rich. They had no reason to feel as if they had a status to protect. But Virginia acknowledges that in the Army School they were given certain privileges and opportunities that were rather unusual for the time. This is illustrated by the particular self-confidence Virginia and a colleague demonstrated during the preparations for their graduation parade. The students were taught to march so that they could march as a body and keep step and move round corners, because their graduation was going to be a grand occasion. 'Everybody was invited as far as I know that was anybody in Washington DC.' Virginia was sent with another student to invite the Vice President and the Secretary of State for Defence to the ceremony. 'A big limousine as long as this room was sent up for us, a big black limousine, and two of us — they picked two little Southern women who they thought would appeal to these men whom we were being sent to invite to our graduation. I was sent to invite the Vice President and General Pershing, the head of the Army, who was then Secretary of Defence. He was in this enormous white panelled office with a great flag over the mantlepiece and a beautiful blue carpet on the floor. The Vice President was in the Capitol Building in an equally huge office, sitting behind the biggest desk I have ever seen. It seemed to be a quarter of a mile we had to walk to get there.'

They went to see the Vice President (Calvin Coolidge) 'a very shy and quiet man'. He kept his hands together all the time they were there and gave them the feeling from the minute they walked into the room that he wanted them to get out as soon as possible. So they came right to the point and asked him if he would come to the graduation and he said that he would like to come but that his wife usually went to things like that with him and she would be out of town, and he doubted therefore whether he could come, Virginia recalls. 'I, like an idiot, said, "Oh Mr Vice President, I thought that was the very time then!" I tried to make a joke about it but he didn't smile at all. I realised my joke had fallen quite flat. Anyway, we got out of there as soon as we could!'

They then went over to the War Department driven in this wonderful car and were invited into General Pershing's room. He was from Texas and he got out from behind his desk and strode across the room to meet them. They came to the point immediately and invited him. His reception was different, as Virginia says, 'I can just see him, with his arms across each of our shoulders, and he said he would come on two conditions, and we said "What are they?" He said, "Both of you must dance with me." That was the difference between the New Englander (Vice President) and the Southerner (General). The difference was reversed at the Final Ball. At the Ball the Vice President came and walked through the room but General Pershing sent his equerry and he didn't come at all!' So that, Virginia argues, is a comment really on the manners of the Northerner and the Southerner: 'The conscience of the New Englander made him come and walk through our party, and General Pershing didn't feel that it was necessary.'

Those Final parades made them feel that nursing was important. They had a pageant for that ceremony, which was written by a classmate. The theme was based on the fact that they had come from the four corners of the globe to go through this Army School. The students were trained in a ballet based on four winds: East, West, South and North. It was presented in a big amphitheatre outdoors, filled with people. 'It was tremendous,' Virginia says, 'and the Marine Band was playing for us. I was the leader of the West wind and had on a flimsy ballet costume made of chiffon and a band round my hair. I had been very much flattered by this woman who trained us because she said I was a natural dancer. Well, I was just imitating the people whom I had seen dancing ballets. I am sure I was ridiculous but it was a lot of fun. The West wind came in with her troupe: then the worst storm I have ever seen broke up the pageant!'

Miss Goodrich gave a most magnificent address and the presiding officers of the Army Hospital participated in the ceremonies. It was magnificent. Supreme Court Justice MacReynolds, a friend of Virginia's father, came too with her father, which greatly flattered her. He said that Miss Goodrich's graduation address to that class was the best public address that he had ever heard given. It really was a magnificent occasion and afterwards they were all served a very nice lunch.

All this pomp and pageantry showed the status that was accorded that class of graduating student nurses. 'Perhaps it gave us considerable self-confidence in future years', thinks Virginia. 'I am not sure that it didn't have some influence on us to have our Final Ball in what was the most elegant hotel in Washington, and to have the Marine Band playing at the ceremony for graduation and for the pageant, and to have a lot of very distinguished people participating in it.'

The social acceptance of nurses was taken for granted by Virginia and her colleagues, to some extent, because they were feted as students in the Army School of Nursing and mixed freely with the social elite in Washington DC. Just as 'nursing in England is made much easier by the participation of the Royal Family and the most distinguished people in the events that you have', Virginia points out. 'I thought the treatment of people at Queen's Nursing Institute's Centenary Conference in London in 1987 was outstanding; the service in Westminster Abbey, and the fact that I was introduced to Princess Diana. It was the sort of acceptance of the value of nursing and the public image of the nurse that I think has given the nurses in England more confidence in fighting their political battles than they have in most countries.'

Virginia suggests that although she was aware of the high status accorded to nurses and nursing in America in the First World War, she feels nurses' status has suffered somewhat since then; but she readily concedes that the Army School was privileged. There, the nursing students were treated like the cadets at West Point Military Academy.

In every army installation there is a social programme provided in a special building set aside for recreation where they have dances periodically. The nurses were able then to talk with the officers, who were the doctors on the wards they worked on. They were able to meet them on common ground. 'All of us had an awfully nice time', Virginia recalls nostalgically. They also had basketball teams and played against other teams. There were tennis courts and many opportunities for pleasant activities when they were off duty. Virginia thinks they had an extremely pleasant life when they were not working; there was no real deprivation for the students in the Army School but she did not feel that the student nurses in the civil hospitals had the same opportunities. But in all the hospitals and visiting nurse agencies in the big cities there were also wonderful opportunities for recreation and they could not possibly feel sorry for themselves or feel deprived. 'You used to wish the day was twice as long to do all the things you wanted to do that were available to you.' Even Virginia's passionate interests in sewing were in abeyance until she had home leave. 'They simply flew out of the window.'

Although Virginia did not develop any new interests during her student days, she saw so much more theatre then when living in Virginia and acquired a taste for going to the theatre, and her reading interests were very much broadened. As she puts it: 'I probably read about more kinds of people with more understanding than I would have had if I had stayed in one part of the country.' And adds: 'I think I always had a great liking for biographies, reading about people. People have been my greatest interest in life.' She has always liked philosophical writing and novels, and still does, but reads fewer of them now than she was younger, much to her regret. 'I don't know that I can say that my experience as a nurse has influenced my taste in literature but I have had to read so much related to my work that I feel a little guilty when I indulge in the kind of reading I enjoy very much, but which is not related to health care.'

CHAPTER 4

Registered Nurse —
Early Experiences

Virginia was restive under the restrictions put on both patients and nurses in institutions and preferred the freedom offered by nursing through community health agencies in which the patient really had control, and could either accept or reject nursing services, according to whether they were valuable to them. After graduation, she planned to work as a private nurse in community agencies. So the first opportunity of employment that she sought was with the Henry Street Settlement, New York, as a visiting nurse. But first, after graduation, she took five months off and her friends came and visited her in Virginia and had a whale of a time. She also visited them and their relatives, and it was a wonderful change. Her family was splendid in making her friends feel welcome and giving her an opportunity to do many things that she had not had time to do for over three years.

Then Virginia went to work soon after Christmas in 1921 and lived with two of her Army School of Nursing friends. The two sisters had found a very attractive apartment on the East side of New York. All three worked with the Henry Street Settlement. One friend (Lucy) afterwards became a social worker. The other friend (Daphne) stayed in nursing and became a teaching supervisor in one of the units at the Henry Street Settlement in the Bronx. Virginia worked there until the summer of 1922 when Miss Goodrich asked her to take charge of a summer camp for children because the person who was supposed to take it had fallen sick and Virginia was to substitute for her.

That summer camp was a very difficult and traumatic time because it was so demanding. She was also in very low and poor health and became sick as a consequence of it. When the person came back from sick leave to take charge after Virginia had been there for about a month she went home and was not very well for a month or two — 'just really recovering from that exhausting experience'. After that she went to work in Washington DC with the Visiting Nurses' Association rather than going back to New York.

It was particularly exhausting running that camp for children held in the house of a private family 'without very much except money' for about thirty little children. With these children came three mothers who were first generation people from Mediterranean countries. Those three mothers were supposed to be helpers. There was also a recreational director — a young woman who would play games with the children. There was also a cook who was absolutely useless. In fact, Virginia had two cooks before she got a third that could do the work. One cook was an old Irish woman, 'alive with bedbugs crawling up her blouse' — she didn't last long! Finally, the thing began to run decently and Virginia got enough people to help so that when she turned it over to the other person she felt as if she had got it into fair shape. The children were quite a problem. Virginia had to put the children to bed and she would find that they still had packed away in their mouths the food from the meals, thought good for them, but they weren't used to eating it. They didn't like it and as they couldn't spit it out, the poor little things went to bed with their cheeks packed full of food. Bread was the only food familiar to them; she tried to give them stewed fruit, cereals and new things that she thought were good for them, but, alas, it was not what they wanted at all.

It was an uphill job getting the bedbugs out of the house. The sofa that Virginia slept on was so full of bedbugs that she could hardly get to sleep at night. Bedbugs, Virginia points out, were a curse to underprivileged and poor people and were rife in those days. During that period she worked about sixteen hours a day helping these small children to eat their meals, finding something they would eat, putting them to bed at night and telling them goodnight stories. She adds: 'They were not tamed really! It was a terrific challenge, but exhausting.' Exhausting it certainly was, as she says, 'I think I was half-sick when I left, and when I got home I think the family realised that I needed considerable rest before I undertook another job.'

At this stage Virginia had no clearly defined idea or plans of the way her future career might develop except that she thought she was going to stay with patient care through a community agency rather than through an institution. The reason she did not stay in community nursing was because she was persuaded by other people who saw in her some qualities she never thought she had. Virginia came from a family of teachers and she thought it would be a good idea if she did something besides teaching. 'So I wasn't going to teach. I was going to practise nursing. That wasn't turning against the family tradition, it was just that I suppose I wanted to have my own life to some extent, and I thought this was an interesting and constructive thing.'

Around this time, as Virginia wanted to be able to practise in Virginia, she took the State Board examinations to become a registered nurse in Virginia, and obtained a very high grade. Because of the grade she was brought to the attention of Ethel Smith who had trained at one of the New York hospitals (St Luke's) when Miss Goodrich was the Director of Nursing there. She saw that Virginia had also been influenced by Miss Goodrich and she recognised in Miss Goodrich a very superior leadership. Therefore, because of the grade and Virginia's association with Miss Goodrich, Miss Smith believed that Virginia could make a major contribution to nursing education if she could be persuaded to work in a school of nursing in the State of Virginia. Virginia thinks she agreed because it seems to have been her nature to let other people recognise in her something that they needed or wanted. 'I have accepted invitations rather than have sought opportunities. I don't know whether it is my character or it must be to some extent a lack of confidence in what I can do. Other people seemed to have more confidence in what I could do than I had myself.'

Before returning to the State of Virginia she spent a period working in the Washington DC Visiting Nurses' Association (in about 1923). She was put into an area of Washington where people lived in impoverished conditions. As the houses have since been renovated into fair sized houses, it does not seem like the poor district it was when she was stationed on the East side, very near the Capitol Building. Many of the people had newly arrived from other countries. She also had many black patients on her roster of patients and some were living in very sad circumstances.

There were many maternity patients at home, who were kept in bed following the birth of a child in that era. The other physical conditions that she took care of were children with communicable disease and people with pneumonia. She enjoyed it very much. She believes the Visiting Nurses' Associations for that age were as popular a voluntary agency as ever existed. Wealthy people contributed to the VNAs and they always had a Board of Directors made up of wealthy people. People were very generous in their support. Much of the service was given freely to patients but also the insurance agencies, like the Metropolitan Life Insurance, gave to their subscribers free care and they paid for visiting nurse agencies to take care of their subscribers. Although many of the poor people couldn't really afford to subscribe to insurance agencies, many did. Virginia supposes that 'there was a certain protection for them. Maybe it was a great draw for them to have home-care. At any rate, I am sure the many of the patients I went to were paid by the Metropolitan Life. Many of them were *very* poor.'

Virginia regrets that although there are still some Visiting Nurses' Associations, as the salaries of the nurses have been so much increased, very few of the voluntary visiting nurse agencies can afford to give care to patients by an RN. 'A home visit is just more than anybody but a well-to-do person can afford these days.' Unlike in Virginia's days, today, RNs doing visiting nurse work in the USA go to see a family, assess them and then send for the kind of help that they can afford, 'which is usually an untrained person or an aide of some sort.' Although these days patients make more office visits, in Virginia's time the people who came to the headquarters of the Visiting Nurse Agencies to see the nursing staff were the pregnant women who came for pre-natal classes or the mothers who brought their well children to the well-baby clinics. 'Now I think they are much more likely to have clinic visitors and pay a small fee for a clinic visit and they get advice. They rarely get any physical care.' In Virginia's day if any of these families had no way of paying, they were not refused care: but there was not a great deal of free care given.

All Virginia's visiting nurse colleagues were RNs when she was in public health nursing. Most of them had post-basic training in public health work. Public health work was a speciality that was most respected. In fact, Virginia claims that the nursing leadership of the USA in the American Nurses' Association (ANA) and National League for Nursing (NLN) was more likely to be from former public health nurses than nurses from hospital administration or teaching. In Washington, Virginia worked five days a week, 8.30 a.m. to 4.30 p.m. and received $2–3000 per annum.

Virginia often digresses to talk about salaries: 'When I went to teach at a school in Virginia I got $3,500 which was, I thought, a very good salary for that day. I was interested in reading Lewis Thomas' book in which he mentions his father's work as a doctor. I think he mentions a $6000-income for a doctor as typical for that era. So in relationship to medicine we were much better paid then than we are now. The doctor's pay now is about five times more than the average nurse's.' Virginia Henderson is always perceptive.

In those days in Washington visiting nurses rarely saw doctors but they had telephonic communication with them. A nurse could only see a family two or three times at the most without them having a doctor, and she could not continue to keep the family on her list without them having a doctor. The patient's regimen was prescribed by the physician but, actually, the doctor's orders did not influence too much what nurses did. Of course, if a hypodermic injection was prescribed, nurses gave it, and they checked to ensure that prescribed medication was taken by the patients.

Doctors participated in the clinic for the well babies. There were always some doctors involved. There was a perfectly good rapport between doctors and nurses, even though some deference was expected, but not surprisingly rejected by Virginia. 'We were taught a foolish kind of thing, I think, like never using a disease term when you talked to a doctor. You were not supposed to say, "We think the third child is catching measles", although we might know perfectly well what to look for. I never paid any attention to that. I thought it was so foolish that I never hesitated to call up the doctor and say "Dr So-and-So, I think the third child has measles." They never showed any displeasure to me!'

That was the period of Mrs Breckenridge's demonstration of the effect of having well-prepared nurses and there were very often midwives from England on her staff. Her work in Kentucky, to Virginia's eternal regret, has never been exploited to demonstrate the worth and extension of that midwifery service in the mountains of Kentucky with well-prepared nurse midwives, serving mainly in the capacity of midwives in maternity work, and also serving as health advisers to the whole family.

Those midwives lived all over that region in which their work was involved. They lived in houses where they had a little clinic in a room, to which everybody in their area could come for help. Virginia travelled around that area, so she speaks from first-hand knowledge. R.S. Dublin studied the first 1000 births in Breckenbridge's Kentucky midwifery service and there was only one death. It was an extraordinary accomplishment for those nurse-midwives, as Virginia constantly argues.

In the 1920s in Washington home deliveries were not uncommon. The doctor was delighted to have the visiting nurses follow-up. Virginia feels sure that many mothers she took care of had been delivered at home. They also did some follow-up care after hospital delivery. Mothers were kept in bed for a week or ten days.

There were the same racial tensions in those days as now, Virginia recalls: 'I would say the relationship between black and white people then was difficult. I felt more of a barrier between the black patients that I took care of in Washington and myself than I felt between any other group that I nursed. It was distressing in some cases with the feeling of lack of warmth and the difficulty you had in establishing a good communicating relationship between them and you. I was very sympathetic with the blacks. I think they had been very badly treated and I think they expected patronage from white people, and they were prepared for it by rejecting you before you rejected them.' But, as Virginia points out, tension between black and white people has always been very noticeable in Washington because there is such a large population of blacks. 'The white population is a little bit threatened by the number of blacks in that city', she believes.

Some of her colleagues, however were black nurses and Virginia has always been very proud of the fact that between black nurses and white nurses she has seen less antagonism and more wholesale acceptance than between any other groups of citizens — black and white. For instance, at the time Virginia went into nursing in the State of Virginia, nurses would not hold a convention in a city where they could not get non-discriminatory treatment for black nurses. However, she encountered discriminatory episodes such as when they had a group picture taken. The photographer would put the black nurses at the end of the line, and even cut them off before he published them in the paper.

Although Virginia concedes that there was probably abuse among children in the 1920s, it was not talked about, nor was it an issue. It came as a terrific shock to her later to have black women open up and talk to her about their abuse, as children and afterwards, by white men. They had probably been afraid of abuse by white men but felt so helpless in the face of the public racial attitude, Virginia feels.

The visiting nurses were happy moving around in Washington. Virginia was not afraid. She felt that with her nurse's uniform on and the bag in her hand, the population was so grateful and had so much respect for nurses that nurses were not afraid to go anywhere.

CHAPTER 5

Back to the State of Virginia as a Teacher

Virginia Henderson was so sure that she was going to have a career in public health nursing that she was totally unprepared for going into teaching. Then, when she accepted Miss Smith's invitation and went to Norfolk Protestant Hospital School she found she was the first full-time nurse instructor in the State of Virginia. Very soon she became the chairman of the Educational Section for the State and she became very much involved with Ethel Smith in raising the standard of nurse education in the State of Virginia — to such an extent that when a man named Frank Bone, the Commissioner for eleven hospitals, spoke at a conference, Virginia got up and followed him out to seek his sympathetic ear. She was trying to promote two things with him: the affiliation of the schools of nursing with the mental hospitals so that students could begin to get experience in psychiatric nursing; and getting a collegiate affiliation for the schools of nursing, and setting up some trial programmes that would use the educational facilities of William and Mary University to further the participation of nursing students in the Norfolk School with extramural courses — or at least start a link between the colleges and the schools of nursing. But that was not to happen for many years until Virginia had gone on to Teacher's College; nonetheless, as she says: 'At least we were talking about it.' Ethel Smith pointed out to Virginia that, as there were no full-time instructors in the State of Virginia, the schools needed a tremendous amount of hard work. She stressed that Virginia was a native of Virginia and made her feel that the fate of the schools of nursing there really rested on her shoulders. So Virginia returned to her home State in 1923.

Miss Smith had formerly been the Director of the Nursing Service and the School at Norfolk Protestant Hospital, where she had voluntarily put on a demonstration of what it would mean to a school to have a full-time instructor. One of Miss Smith's pupils, Caroline Brickhouse, was the Director when Virginia arrived. She looked on Miss Smith as a great leader, just as Virginia looked on Miss Goodrich. Almost anything Miss Smith said at that hospital and School of Nursing went unquestioned. Virginia supposes she, as an outsider, was 'quite a cross to bear' to the people in that hospital. The nurses who graduated from that hospital saw nothing wrong with what was going on there. Virginia, however, had entirely different ideas and it was pretty hard on them.

Virginia Henderson RN went to Norfolk Hospital with absolutely no preparation for teaching other than that she came from a teaching family. She seems to have taken to it like a duck to water because it was as happy a period of her life as any she can identify. It certainly developed a fighting spirit in her — for what she thought would be good for the students and the patients. She had such a struggle.

Miss Ethel Smith was also struggling to get recognition for the importance of reform in nursing education. She and another public health nurse — Agnes Randell — were great rivals; 'perhaps friendly rivals but it gave the feeling that you couldn't really be in both camps!' You could either be loyal to one or the other but could not be loyal to both. That was hard for Virginia because the Randell family was very well-known to her family and she recognised in Agnes Randell an natural born Southern leader. 'She could have been one of the Confederate Generals easily.' She had a tremendous following. She had prevented single-handed, as Virginia understood it, the formation of a State League for Nursing Education.

The only thing nurses had in the State of Virginia was an Educational Section and that was led by Ethel Smith. Virginia feels sure she was responsible for making her chairman of it and she soon began to feel the responsibility for what happened at the State Convention.

Norfolk Hospital was totally unlike any hospital that Virginia had ever been associated with in her student experience. It was a matriarchy. Miss Brickhouse ruled that place with great assurance. She could do almost anything that had to be done in the hospital. Virginia believes Miss Brickhouse 'could have done a very nice little operation if she had been allowed to! She could give anaesthetics. I am sure she was a superb clinical nurse but with no preparation except what she had in that hospital.' The world began and ended in that hospital for Miss Brickhouse; so much so that when Virginia wanted to take the students to other hospitals to see new things, she was opposed: 'I had to be very persuasive and stubborn about certain things. She didn't want them to see what was going on in other hospitals — it wasn't necessary!'

The Director of Nursing lived in the nurses' dormitory. Her head nurses, who had also graduated from that school, adored her and thought that there could not be anything wrong with what she wanted. So anything Virginia wanted to do was only accomplished by persuasion of both the Director and head nurses.

Students did not enter the school once or twice a year; they came in any time. When Virginia arrived there, when the 'senior student' got in an elevator, every other student in the school stood aside — because she had seniority. This student — Miss Bird — was a very able, interesting woman and Virginia had real respect for her, which also satisfied Miss Bird. Virginia began to insist on students coming in twice a year on a regular basis instead of dribbling into school throughout the year. It would have been impossible otherwise for Virginia to set up any sort of curriculum. Although she quickly retorts, with great amusement, when the topic of curriculum development is raised: 'I don't think I had ever heard the word "curriculum" before I went to that school, and I didn't know that such things as a "curriculum guide" existed. One was published in the USA first in 1917 and revised in 1927 and again in 1937. When I was at Teacher's College we were doing the '37 Edition and I participated in it, so that by that time I got saturated with what was in it'. Virginia supposes Ethel Smith must have told her about the 1917 curriculum. It was called a 'Standard Curriculum' in the first edition. 'I suppose no book has ever looked this good to somebody as that "Standard Curriculum" looked to me, because I must have been floundering terribly!' It was published by the National League for Nursing Education (now called the National League for Nursing). That curriculum was Virginia's salvation and she began to plan a course for the students based on what was recommended in it.

There were about a dozen students in Virginia's first class. Her own words are vivid:

'Now when I went there, there was not a book; the skeleton we used for teaching anatomy was hanging in a big room that was a solarium and the room should have been available to the patients, but was used for whatever teaching Miss Smith had been doing. There was one cupboard in that room; I don't remember anything in it really, but there may have been some nursing equipment. I don't remember any running water in that room, but there must have been. Later it was turned into a children's ward but that was not until I got one end of the basement converted into about a five- or six-roomed teaching department. I began working on that almost immediately. For the first year I taught in that solarium. That was where I gave my demonstrations. I collected as soon as possible equipment to enable me to teach the students the procedures used on the units.

'I could do anything I wanted there as long as it didn't cost too much money. Miss Brickhouse had an expression that I felt hardened to, but to almost anything I asked for she would say, "I don't know where you will get the money for that." She used to say, "You can go and stick your neck out and ask Mr Pender for the money." I think he was the chairman of the Board. He was a very rich man who had made his money in groceries. I never had any refusal of a request that I made but, of course, I didn't go to him regularly. I only went to him when I had Miss Brickhouse's blessing or permission to go to him. I remember going there very soon after I got there and saying, "Miss Brickhouse, these students haven't anything to do when they get off duty except to go to their rooms in the nurses' home" — which was right in the grounds — "and complain about the things that made them unhappy. I think there ought to be some recreational programme set up for them." One of the first things I would do would be to have a tennis court built in the yard because they could use it and the interns could use it.'

'"Well", she said, "if you want to stick your neck out you can go and ask Mr Pender for the money for it, but I am not going to do it." I went round there soon and got a tennis court established. But it was that way with everything that would cost money. It was like pulling teeth to get money. So much so that when I was distressed with the grimness of the students' dining room, I remember in the summer vacation during a period when I wasn't teaching, painting about ninety chairs black and painting bunches of fruit on them! Which was, of course, absurd, but I was so determined to get some lighter note into the lives of those people, that I enjoyed doing it.

'Looking back on it, I marvel at the number of things Miss Brickhouse let me do. The first thing that I had to do was to get doctors who had been giving lectures in subjects that I knew I could teach better than they were teaching to give up those courses. One man was teaching anatomy and physiology in a series of something like twelve or fifteen lectures. I knew enough about physiology to do a better job than that, and so I made a temporary enemy of that teacher by taking his course away from him. I auditioned all the things that the doctors were teaching, and if I thought that they were not doing a good job, it was really up to me to find a way to eliminate them from the teaching programme. It wasn't easy.'

Virginia absolutely refused to live in the dormitory (nurses' home) which was a great blow to the hospital authority. At her insistence, it was in her letter of acceptance that she could live in town away from the hospital (because she knew that if she lived in that hospital she would have no life other than that). So she lived two or three blocks away in her Uncle Jim's sister's house. Their house was a well-known popular residence because she — and a friend — ran the fashionable girls' school for the city of Norfolk. It gave Virginia an entrée to the life outside the hospital. It would have been a sad thing if they had forced her to live in the school, Virginia believes. The first time that they offered Virginia a salary increase they said they would raise the salary if she came to live in the school. She still refused and they raised it anyway!

As Virginia knew that the United States' Government had a wide range of publications, and that they were all free, she ordered something like several copies of hundreds of pamphlets to place in the library. A truck from the Post Office drew up outside the hospital one day and they began to unload pile after pile after pile. They were placed on shelves set up in the solarium. Each student could have what she wanted from that supply. It amounted to a fairly good professional library for them: there were pamphlets on scarlet fever, measles — you name it. She had taken the Government catalogue and gone through it: that was the first library resource Virginia ever created. Virginia had her own books, of course, which represented the best of the textbooks for the time. Students had textbooks in all the sciences and whatever existed then in the clinical field. 'Maxwell and Pope' was then the basic text in nursing but very soon Virginia learnt of the text of Bertha Harmer, *Text-book of the Principles and Practice of Nursing*, whose first three editions were published in 1922, 1928 and 1934. That textbook opened up a new world to her because Miss Harmer, even in her first edition, based her recommendations for nursing practice on a physiological basis. The physiology textbook written by

Howell was Miss Harmer's bible. Virginia marvels now when she looks at those first editions and to see those pages of Howell that were included. (Virginia Henderson was, some years later, to take over Miss Harmer's textbook as its new author.) Virginia very soon got her hands on the Harmer book and it certainly influenced the way she taught. It was a reliable source and something beyond the usual simplified text for students.

Ethel Smith was responsible for Virginia joining the State Nurses' Association and getting her involved in its work to the extent of helping to plan the meetings. In the first year Virginia invited Miss Goodrich to come and give a lecture to the State meeting. For that State meeting, Virginia did the same trick of ordering all the stock from the Government and had the whole room full of this literature. The free literature made quite a stir because there had never been anything like that at a State meeting and it brought it to the attention of people from all over the State. There were enough copies for everyone who came to the State Convention to help themselves. It was a wonderful free hand-out, full of instructional material. Of course, Ethel Smith was perfectly delighted. Virginia then met all the prominent leaders in the State. She regularly went to State meetings and became very involved in the work in the State. That was very helpful to her because as more instructors were introduced in all the nursing schools, those young instructors and Virginia formed a group 'to struggle together for a while over our problems and we could visit each other.'

In the first year at Norfolk, Virginia was so near the age of the students that she could identify very well with their feelings. So she put a tremendous amount of energy into trying to produce an ethos that enabled them to see and understand other health work in the community. That was completely new and met with great resistance, and taking them to other hospitals and agencies met with resistance. She also took the students on visits to a State mental hospital to enable them to get some feeling that something else was going on beyond the walls of their particular hospital.

The Norfolk Hospital was a very friendly looking place but the black patients were segregated. That was the first experience Virginia had had of the segregation of black patients. She supposes she has blotted out of her mind most of the other horrors of the first year. All she can remember is relishing what she did. It is surprising how many struggles were won; she was sure it was just by persistence and by persuading Miss Brickhouse that she was thinking about the welfare of the students.

Virginia felt the new students ought to have a welcoming party and was allowed to send out an invitation in which there was an announcement of the opening of a cabaret at the address of the hospital. Many people didn't realise what they were being invited to. She had all the furniture removed from the solarium and put little tables all around it. She invited the doctors to be the waiters and to come in costumes, which they did. The menu was made up of all kinds of things; 'but no matter what you ordered you got punch and cakes or something like that!' Somehow or other Virginia enticed an orchestra to come and play, but how she got the money to pay for it, she cannot imagine. People came and they were escorted into this solarium as if it were a cabaret. They had contests in dancing and everybody who came participated. At another welcoming party for the students there was a party on a boat, decorated as a Chinese junk, and another party was held at the nicest club in town. They also had fancy dress parties.

Virginia always had to battle for the students. One was a woman who had been married and had lost her husband and, as a widow, had gone into training. She had several children who were being cared for by her mother. She was a great strength for Virginia because her judgment was excellent. Virginia could talk to her about anything. She was not fond of Miss Brickhouse, she was too independent of spirit. Virginia, nevertheless, supported her. 'The students depended on me and they were my children regardless of every mistake they made and the rules they broke — and they were my little angels. I naturally defended them.'

The first Christmas at Norfolk Virginia asked for a two-week holiday and Miss Brickhouse 'readily agreed because the students would become hers!' When Virginia came back the most promising student was handing in her resignation. She had been put in charge of patients and it was far too early in her training. Senior students nursed the patients: there was no question about that. Virginia initially was horrified by what was expected of the students. The students at the Norfolk Hospital never saw a graduate nurse lay their hands on a patient. They themselves manned the wards and, on the men's wards, they were assisted by black men.

The supervisor on a medical surgical unit brought her embroidery to work every morning and sat at her desk with the head nurse and embroidered. She answered the questions of the students but would not participate with any 'hands on' care. She was the boss. Graduate (trained) nurses did not consider that working with their hands was part of their work. They were not good role models for the students but they were a source of information for them, and technically responsible for anything that happened on their floors. Nevertheless, Virginia says they must have had a means of knowing which students were most able and how to assign patients to the students. That hospital ran on a task assignment basis rather than on the assignment of patients to nurses or students. Some of the nursing was done by private duty nurses; if patients could afford it they had a private duty nurse. And Miss Brickhouse was the supreme ruler!

Virginia very soon persuaded Miss Brickhouse that it would be an advantage if the school were registered in the State of New York. That would allow students to be able to be employed in New York State without having to take their State Board. New York State also had a very high standard and visited hospitals throughout the country, and that guaranteed that the curriculum was preparing people adequately. A request was made for this. The basement was eventually fixed up as educational quarters, which Virginia recalls without difficulty:

> I had a laboratory, a small library, an office for myself and a large classroom. The doctors used to hold their staff meetings in my classroom and leave notes for me on the board, and I did likewise. We kept up a running sparring match! They then decided that they would like to have the whole end of the building that I had fixed up. Bless my soul, they got it, and I had to fix up the other end of the building.
>
> In both cases I had a laboratory where a person teaching chemistry could function and the person teaching bacteriology could teach certain laboratory procedures. There was a big lecture room and a unit was set up like a ward so that I could teaching nursing procedures in that, and a utility room comparable to the ones they would find on the floors. So for the time it was quite adequate. It was quite attractive with curtains and carpets. The atmosphere was very encouraging for the student nurses to work.
>
> As soon as possible I got the pathologist to teach bacteriology and pathology. I had a chemistry teacher from the High School to teach chemistry. I kept the anatomy and physiology because I loved it and because I thought it was so important, and that no one would take the same amount of trouble with it. It was ridiculous to think how little had been taught them because there was a student in one of the classes who came from one of the more advantaged families, and I was teaching something like the physiology of the heart or the intestinal tract, and she was so overcome with hearing about the workings of the body that she fainted!'

Soon after going to Norfolk Hospital, Virginia began going to Teacher's College, New York, for summer sessions and studied anatomy and physiology with Caroline Stackpole. She enjoyed teaching very much but believed that you couldn't be a very informed nurse without a good knowledge of physiology.

Norfolk Hospital had an annual Hospital Day: it was an Open Day, all day long. The students put on demonstrations, like cold packs as used in psychiatry, sponge baths and the use of cold sprays used in the reduction of temperature, and washing people's hair in bed; 'we were very proud of washing people's hair — which people are not taught now.'

Virginia has regrettably recently discovered, as an in-patient, that nurses are not being taught to wash people's hair, so that a patient who is recumbent is out of luck. When she was a teacher, they spent a long period teaching nursing practice and thinks the emphasis on teaching the basic skills really paid off for the graduates of that school. They seemed to get a reputation for giving excellent bedside care. She also thinks it explains the doctors' support for her because when the time came for her to leave, the doctors petitioned Virginia to stay. A few years after she left, Miss Brickhouse resigned and they asked her to come back and take her position as head of the school and service. 'So they must have had some confidence in my capability.'

Virginia arranged clinical experiences for her students at Norfolk Hospital and at a visiting nurse agency. She also planned an affiliation with a psychiatric hospital.

As Virginia was the only instructor, she very soon began to work on the supervisors in obstetrics and paediatrics to help with teaching as 'they were the only supervisors that I can remember who had something to contribute.' Virginia assumed responsibility for the lectures in nursing and surgery with some help from the operating room supervisor for the surgical lectures. She was a very good person in the operating room and gave her students excellent instruction, especially about safe aseptic technique in the operating room. Virginia remembers approaching the obstetrics supervisor and asking her if she would like to chaperone the doctors' lectures on obstetrics, and being asked 'What are you being paid for?' Virginia then realised that as they had a full-time instructor, the supervisors thought that would liberate them from any responsibilities for instruction of students. It took Virginia a little while to persuade them that it would be to everybody's advantage if they would participate in the teaching programme. 'Before I left, I think everybody was participating.'

After the preliminary course of about four months, students had classes for not more than three or four hours a week. The doctors were not paid for the lectures they gave and they did not hesitate to call up and say they could not come, or be late. It was not very satisfactory. The doctors' lectures were followed up with the related nursing procedure for each speciality. Virginia found her teaching commitments were very demanding: 'If you had two intakes, and the introductory courses lasted from four to five months, most of your time would have been taken up with the introductory courses.' She was kept quite busy during the school year with the introductory programme alone — teaching nursing skills, anatomy, physiology and pharmacology.

Because Virginia became involved in the State work and went to all the teaching conventions, she came to the notice of Macmillan, the major publishers of nursing books. The publisher's representatives came with all the books they had published for nurses. Virginia says the representatives were 'very able and engaging young men with these exhibits, being my age and very well-educated and very informed and helpful. I made great friends with these people, so much so, that they furnished me with copies of every single thing they published. Anything I wanted they gave me. So that I began to build up a library with donations from publishers.'

Virginia also got help from the manufacturers of equipment who came to the State meetings and exhibited equipment. Their gifts helped her to build up a really good supply of teaching resources in that department. There were always travelling representatives who came to see what she needed and what she had accomplished. Modestly, Virginia thinks 'they were interested, I wouldn't say impressed, but I think they could certainly see that the students had better than average a place to work and study.'

Doctors and other visitors to Norfolk Hospital often saw Virginia on Saturday and Sunday mornings taking care of patients 'for the purpose of keeping myself competent as a hands-on nurse.' She became very interested in some of these people she cared for at the weekends. 'You see, I came with a public health background so I would try and help these people whom I knew were going to be discharged to take care of themselves. They resented it bitterly. Those patients were sent home really incapacitated by private nurses who were endearing themselves to the patients by giving them 100 per cent care. They were paid for it and patients felt they deserved it, and they wanted it with absolutely no thought of preparing them for independence when they got home.' Nurturing the patient's independence was a theme that Virginia tried to impart into her students but she does not know how successful she was as many of them went into private nursing when they qualified. There were not too many things nurses could do in those days.

Miss Brickhouse kept the selection of candidates in her hands. It was rare to have a college-educated applicant and Virginia cannot recall a single male applicant. There were very few male nurses in the State of Virginia at that time and she cannot remember any male nurses at the nursing conventions. Black women went to nursing schools for black nurses but at the conventions 'we were all mixed up and we had meals together', she points out.

An early proposal that Virginia made to the students was to invite them to consider forming a student government. They thought they would like it and immediately selected the widowed student as the head of it. This made Miss Brickhouse renege on it because she was afraid of her! She considered her far too independent and looked upon her as a troublemaker. 'This woman had opinions and a great deal of professional dignity', Virginia recalls, 'I thought she was great! It nearly broke my heart to tell the students they couldn't have this, and I couldn't tell them why. I just told them that Miss Brickhouse had changed her policy.'

In those days Virginia believed in and practised experiential learning as her words illustrate: 'All these young people had to do these things to each other. I made them be the subjects of the demonstrations I gave and they didn't resist it. They were willing to do it and then they practised on each other. We gave each other sterilised hypodermics. I don't know how sound that was legally. I was determined that they would learn before they did it on the hospital floor. Anyway, I wanted to help them to acquire the skill of giving a hypodermic so that a person almost doesn't feel it. If you pinch the person hard enough before you stick the needle in they feel the pinch which masks the feeling of the needle. They are used to being pinched. Pinches are an affectionate sort of thing; but the needle is the invasion of their body. So I used to teach them to draw up the skin and stick the needle in whilst the patient was responding to the pinch, and they began to realise you could do it so that the person said that they didn't feel the needle.' Virginia thinks they were assured of being safe practitioners by their practice on one other with procedures right from the very beginning of this teaching programme; she feels she did not have enough supervision as a student nurse in doing procedures and that she was afraid to carry them out. That is why she instituted the practice of having students practise on one other before they did procedures on the patients. They also practised putting dressings on wounds and they gave each other enemas, too, to see what it felt like to have one. Virginia tried to persuade the supervisors to make their students watch them doing nursing procedures before they asked the students to do them — but without success. As a result, there were many traumatic experiences for the students.

With some regret Virginia says: 'Even if I could have done all those things myself skilfully enough for the students to learn by watching me doing it, I didn't have the time to do that teaching on the floors. I was more than busy. I don't think many instructors of this age would have considered it a tolerable programme. I literally worked there all day, every day, for five days a week. It was nothing like what I would do now, or hope to see happening in the present schools of nursing.'

The application for approval by the New York State was not successful; but, ever the pragmatist, Virginia used the report to try to do any number of things that she had been begging the hospital authorities to do, but which they had been resisting. The hospital collaborated with Virginia because they desperately wanted to be registered in the State of New York — not so much for the benefit of the nursing graduates as for their pride. So they had another inspection a year or two later and that went through with flying colours. The school by that time had a reputation for producing very competent nurses and some of the better students began to do things that brought the school to the attention of people.

Virginia subsequently got an academic educationalist, Frank Baines, interested in the possibility of connecting that nursing school with the local university. By the 1980s that hospital had grown enormous. A medical school has been established at the Old Dominion University and Norfolk Hospital is being used by medical students. There is also a graduate programme for nurses at the university, which awarded Virginia an Honorary Doctorate in the 1970s.

Virginia considers her five years at Norfolk Hospital to have been 'wonderfully satisfying' — but if asked if she did any writing or research during those five years, she replies immediately, without apology — 'Not a bit. Research, good heavens! All I could do was meet my classes every day. I had to study very hard to know enough to conduct those classes. I had some very smart girls in that school and they would be perfectly capable of taking the textbook we were using and studying it assiduously and being much better than I was! I developed a very healthy respect for student nurses. It was a time-consuming job.'

Writing and research activities were still to come — but much later.

CHAPTER 6

Back to New York City for Further Studies

In 1929 Virginia started to think about going to Teacher's College, Columbia University, in New York City. Increasingly, she began to feel the need for some further higher education. She had been to the summer schools and found them a great help — especially the classes that Caroline Stackpole taught in anatomy and physiology. 'She was a genius as a teacher. If you asked her a question she never came right out and answered it, she made you think. She made you answer yourself if you could. She had a most engaging way of teaching.' In particular, Virginia wanted to get all the science background she could, believing strongly that nursing was based on the biomedical sciences. She also wanted all the social sciences she could get. The curriculum at Teacher's College was generously supplied with psychology; and sociology, which she 'always took with a grain of salt'.

So Virginia left Norfolk Hospital and became a student at Teacher's College, Columbia University. She paid her way with a legacy that her great-aunt left: $1000. She supplemented this with earnings. 'It helped a great deal when I applied for part-time employment.' The head of the home economics department wanted someone to live in her apartment in her guest room. Her mother was a diabetic and needed to take insulin every morning. She also needed somebody to stay and read to her mother when she was away in the evenings. 'It was a wonderful help to me because she had a Bermudan cook who was one of the best cooks I have ever known and a lovely person. She used to bring my breakfast in bed.' Another good thing for Virginia was that, by then, her Uncle Jim was a professor of physical optics in New York and had his office across the street from Teacher's College and lived about two blocks away. She visited him and his wife regularly for meals.

Miss Sally Johnson, who had been the Director of the Walter Reed unit of the Army School of Nursing, also came there to study; she was then middle-aged. Virginia was delighted to see her because she now felt able to tell her how terribly she had treated Virginia when she was a student. 'I thought she had a real prejudice against Southern women and I felt she was much harder on me than she was on anybody else in the class. She did all sorts of things that went against the grain with me, including telling me to bring my brush and comb with me and to come to her room, and she re-arranged my hair. Of course, it didn't take me very long to get it right back where it had been before! Those were some of the things that I had to tell Miss Sally Johnson.' Fortunately, Miss Johnson just laughed and told Virginia that her students were probably then saying just the same things about her. They ended up sharing meal-times at the same table in the dining room of the college.

Virginia took thirty-two units a year and was not allowed to take more, but she managed to incorporate tap dancing, as an extra, into her programme. 'I enjoyed that tremendously! I still love watching other people tap dancing.'

Virginia did as much science as she could, including physics, chemistry, physiology, anatomy and bacteriology. Courses in teaching methods were compulsory as were courses on the application of Edward Thorndike's principles of education to nursing. She greatly admired Thorndike and thinks his teaching on the needs of man was very constructive and very influential in her final analysis of what nursing was because 'I said we do for others what they would do for themselves if they had sufficient strength of will and the knowledge. I was thinking about their human needs and that is compatible with the teachings of Thorndike on the needs of man. He influenced me as a teacher as well as a nurse. His influence was profound.' She also had English and history courses and mathematics, including statistics (which she never really liked, but passed in due course). The course that 'opened doors' to her was the physics course. 'I didn't learn many of the secrets of physics but I learnt some of the practical things that everybody could learn. Like learning how to wire up a plug. I think it was the only thing that I learnt at Teacher's College that impressed my family!' What impressed Virginia about the physics course was the practical application of principles of physics. Many of the classes were taken with other groups from other disciplines.

Miss Isabel Stewart, a Canadian nurse, was then the head of the nursing department at Teacher's College. 'She was a lovely person. I always felt that I knew Miss Stewart quite well — as if we were good friends. I suspect that she had done very little nursing but had gone into teaching almost directly after she had graduated from one of the Canadian schools. I think she was a natural born teacher.' She was an intellectual and her writings were very helpful to all the nursing profession, Virginia recalls. Miss Stewart was the moving spirit 'in the religion of what was called a Standard Curriculum'. But this curriculum guide was last published in 1937 when it was thought that it was too restricting. Miss Stewart was also a leading spirit in the National League for Nursing.

Virginia cannot recall how radical her ideas were during the first year that she was at Teacher's College 'but evidently I did not make too many waves'. She had a delightful life there and if she went there with any Southern prejudices they were certainly challenged as she was thrown together with Asians, black people and many others. Teacher's College was really a Mecca, in her view, and its nursing programme was more or less unique. Virginia believes that Teacher's College prepared more nurse leaders than any other programme. Certainly at her time it was almost unchallenged.

Virginia was at Teacher's College for just a year before the money ran out, but was given credit for the courses as she expected to go back and complete her course and get a degree. She decided that she wanted to see what was going on in a big general hospital but she did not want to lose her interest in what happened to the patient at home. At that time she was still determined to go into public health nursing eventually. She thought it would be good for her to work in a large hospital in a larger place, for a change, and perhaps in a hospital connected with a collegiate programme. She applied for a position at the Strong Memorial Hospital, Rochester, which was associated with a collegiate nursing programme at Rochester University. She was appointed to a post in the hospital's out-patient department; a Miss Peterson, of Norwegian descent, was the person in charge of the whole department.

Patients could walk in for out-patient treatment. Mostly they were people who had been previously treated in the hospital. There was also an ante-natal clinic. There were teaching classes for patients similar to the classes in a public health service, familiar to Virginia. She was the first teaching supervisor they had in that department; in fact, it was a kind of joint clinical/teaching appointment. Virginia taught both nursing students and patients. She was given a totally free hand by Miss Peterson, in spite of the latter being 'quite a martinet — more concerned with tidiness than anything else!' Virginia used to go the library and borrow relevant books and place them in the teaching room. The books contained health and other information pertinent to the patients, and included information about the treatments that were being given to the patients. 'The students were taught to feel free and go in there and study during their eight-hour day in that out-patient department. They were not made to feel that they had to work every minute.' For patients, she set up permanent exhibits. In a paediatric clinic they had a splendid exhibit for mothers; Virginia then found manufacturers willing to give her anything that she wanted. 'I think people marvelled to see students during a working day taking time off to look something up.'

In Rochester, Virginia found the community so well-organised from the standpoint of health care that she began to go monthly to community health meetings at which a representative of every community health agency in that city met and talked about the problems of the community. It was (and remains) a unique experience for Virginia. 'They met in a place that was large enough for us to have lunch together. People made reports from the agencies that they represented. I could get the co-operation of anybody there in teaching students.' It was a delightful life in Rochester for Virginia.

They were about half a mile from a river and it had a large enough area for a skating rink in winter. She used to go skating some afternoons; it amazed her colleagues that somebody from the South could skate on ice! But she had developed the skill of skating as a child.

Very often at weekends Virginia worked as a volunteer nurse just to see how the units ran and to see what was going on. The unit that she enjoyed particularly was the very well-run psychiatric unit. The patient conferences particularly impressed her and influenced the way she was later to teach nursing, even though at Rochester they did not have the patient present as Virginia did later. But she saw the value of having everybody who was taking care of the patient pool their opinions and knowledge. The psychiatrist was a very democratic person and believed that the nurses' input was of value so that student nurses were not afraid to express an opinion or contribute something that they had observed. 'Those patient conferences were a lesson to me because I had never seen anything that was as good as that.' Anybody who contributed to the care of the patient was invited to come to the conference for it was their belief that unless they were working as a team to help that patient they were really not giving optimum care. 'There was nothing horrifying about the care of patients in that unit. My lasting impression of the place [psychiatric hospital] that I nursed in as a student was that if you were not crazy when you went there, you were crazy when you left. It was enough to make anybody go mad.'

It was not like that at Rochester; psychiatric patients were dressed in street clothes, although the unit was a locked unit. Some were allowed to come and go freely and were let in and out by a staff member. 'As in all parts of the hospital, the meals were delicious.'

Virginia's main responsibility was seeing that the students learnt from the opportunity to see out-patient care given. She felt that they could not learn as much as there was to be learnt there unless she brought into that out-patient department some of the teaching that she had seen done in visiting nurse work. That is why she set up teaching exhibits to encourage the people who were running the clinics to teach patients regularly. Virginia remembers one particular head nurse who 'encouraged me and she looked at the exhibits in the paediatric department and said it was doing more for patients than they did. The doctors were also pleased with these teaching exhibits, which we changed from time to time.' She recalls a teaching session for the patients with syphilis on Saturdays, because that was when workers could come. 'I can remember the nurse who was in charge of that clinic and who actually gave the injections. She functioned as another intern. In those days student nurses were afraid of the contagious possibilities of syphilis. I was disapproving at first of the nurse doing exactly the same as the doctors but she was super skilful with her injections. She was marvellous.'

The staff in each clinic encouraged the nurses there to develop a teaching programme and to participate with Virginia in teaching the students. She worked through the graduate head nurses as much as she could and encouraged the graduate nurses to teach the students. Virginia was also very happy to run their clinics so that they could undertake these teaching duties. 'I suppose there was a residue of that pedagogy that I used for ever after. I didn't scorn all of it. I did become much more aware of the effective approaches to learning — and the ineffective. I suppose I am such an individualist that I resent doing anything by rule, but I think that I learnt that you are much more effective if you encourage people by praise than criticism. I was very much touched because my nephew, who is a professor of classics and a very fine teacher, on occasions has lived with me for short periods, when he was in the navy during the war and when he came back my apartment was home for him in New York; he lived with me when he started teaching in New York before his family joined him. Not too long ago he credited me with having taught him that praise was more effective than blame. He pulled me up sharp because he thought I was blaming somebody.'

During her year at Rochester, one experience there has had a life-long influence on Virginia. She was introduced to the concept of psychosomatic medicine. Although she is not able to identify precisely the influence on her ideas about the nature of nursing, she argues that psychosomatic medicine has certainly been a very dominant influence in her life. 'I believe that the influence of mind over matter is something that we still have not grasped the importance of. I don't think many people in nursing and medicine practise with anything like an adequate concept of how much illness is psychic and how much is physical — or how much your thought influences the way your body works. I read a great deal that year, partly because I was searching for things that I thought would influence the students to have a broader concept.'

After nearly a year at Rochester, Virginia had a letter from Miss Stewart saying that she thought Virginia ought to come back and finish her degree. She obtained a Rockefeller Scholarship 'which was more money than I had ever had. It was enough to make it possible for me to study at Teacher's College.' The Rockefeller Foundation financed the rest of Virginia's course of study at Teacher's College, which awarded her first a Bachelor's degree and than a Master's degree.

CHAPTER 7

Virginia Returns to Teacher's College

In 1932 Virginia resumed her studies at Teacher's College. She had an instructorship at Teacher's College when she went back, even before she obtained her Bachelor's degree, so the income from teaching supplemented the Rockefeller Scholarship.

Very soon after she went back there she found she had exhausted all the possibilities of advanced study in the sciences but she still wanted more. She then managed to go up to the Columbia Presbyterian University Medical School and persuaded them to let her take anatomy and physiology courses with the medical students. That was an additional help to her because it was taught along experimental lines and students were encouraged to experiment on each other. This enriched Virginia for she got 'the feeling of the way the body worked because we did use each other as subjects. Also I learned to be sceptical about the teachings of some of the textbooks. I developed a questioning approach to the study of scientific subjects.'

Virginia was the only nurse but not the only woman among the medical students. She must have been very well-prepared to take the course because when she went up to take the examination she was amazed to find herself on the list of those excused from writing the examination. She was awarded credits at Teacher's College for the work she did in the Medical School.

She also took an advanced course in bacteriology at the Postgraduate Hospital and took as much as she could in that programme. Nursing courses and educational theory and practice courses were taken at Teacher's College (including practical application at a local hospital school of nursing).

At Teacher's College, in those days, students took examinations at the end of each course. In the Master's programme they did not have to write a thesis but Virginia elected to do so. She obviously had a very good grounding in anatomy, physiology, microbiology and the medical and biological sciences. She regularly says — over and over again — that these days nurses are losing out because they do not have that grounding in the biological sciences and this lack is distorting their practice of nursing. Although she was also taught sociology and psychology, the social sciences, she argues, have tended to dominate nursing recently since the time when nurses decided 'to put nursing on a research basis', which in her view 'is a pretentious assumption'. Nurses cannot have enough research as a base for everything they do, she constantly argues, for in her view, to worship research is an absurdity. 'We began literally to worship research and to feel that we would never arrive at being a profession unless we based our practice on research, the assumption being that medicine did that, which was another absurdity.'

Nurses then, she recalls, began to try to get people to help them with research. The first studies nurses knew anything about were surveys and recommendations that came from the people who made the surveys. 'They were usually social scientists!' That was nurses' introduction to research and nurses were encouraged, she believes, to look upon these surveys as typical of the research that would be useful to them. This made it very difficult, she argues, for those nurses who were interested in clinical nursing to get doctors to work with them as partners in clinical research.

Whereas the social scientists in the USA were perfectly delighted to have a bridge into the hospital, because in the USA 'writing and talking' is the sociologists' way of making a living. 'You don't think of them as doers. They are not part of the service team.' So Virginia thinks that they were delighted to get into the hospital, working with nurses. When she began to work with the sociologists and anthropologists she was taken to their conventions. She recalls, 'I would feel like a spy almost, because they did not know that I was a nurse and they would say things like: "Why don't you charge the nurses? They have got a lot of money for research".' With some concern, Virginia points out that many American nurses got Doctor's degrees in the social sciences in the early 'research' days when doctoral degrees in nursing were not available. It followed that those nurses who had Doctor's degrees in sociology, anthropology or psychology or who had been helped by a member of a university faculty in social sciences, would naturally emphasise these disciplines when they began teaching. Hence the dominance of social sciences in the nursing curriculum.

Nursing practice suffered as a result of that, Virginia believes, to the extent that the physiological approach to the patient was neglected. 'It was at that time that our language became loaded with jargon and you were helpless unless you knew this language. A textbook came out then telling the students that they would have to learn fifty-seven new terms. Most of them were the terms of the social scientist.'

In her Master's programme, Virginia took the more advanced courses in the methods of teaching and also did a lot of research in bacteriology. At that time the chief causes of death were respiratory infections, and the control of communicable disease was very much part of nurses' work. Virginia was particularly interested in the difference in the practices in relation to sterilisation of dressings etc., in hospitals and the trend towards buying ready-made sterilised supplies. The bacteriologist at Johnson & Johnson was very helpful and advised her; she was persuaded even before she started that steam under pressure was so much more effective than boiling.

As a result of her research interest, she also began to see environmental

48

health as an extremely important part of health work, and this was also probably due to her interest in public health nursing in the community. 'I was impatient with the people who worked in the hospitals who seemed to think that anything important in health was done in the hospitals. I realised it was very important to teach the public the ways of preventing illness. The public looked on the doctors as dramatic healers and the nurse as the doctor's assistant. I felt we were disregarding what the nutritionists and environmentalists were teaching us.'

Virginia did a very rigorous comparative study of boiling and sterilising instruments by steam. She first attempted to contaminate them with spores 'because you couldn't say any method was good unless it destroyed the spores.' Sometimes she had to use rabbits in the experiments, which she disliked, for the growth of spores. What she learned about practices of sterilisation was persuasive. She also reviewed various national sanitary codes. She was amazed that her supervisor thought the report of the research was good enough to be put into a bulletin that was published by the department of nursing.

Virginia's research supervisor (Miss Stewart) became convinced that she could write well. That is possibly responsible for the fact that when Miss Harmer (who had written the text that Virginia had used in nursing teaching) died, Miss Stewart advised the publishers that Virginia Henderson was well suited to take on responsibility for the next (fourth) edition, which she did, even though: 'I had no leave of absence to do that. I know I worked on it during my summer vacation and I must have worked on it in the evenings or when I wasn't teaching. It was a terrific labour to undertake with no leave of absence.' The fourth edition appeared in 1939.

After graduating as an MA, Virginia remained on the faculty at Teacher's College. She participated in a great range of courses as an assistant and also had her own courses, including introduction to research techniques. She really wanted to do something that was clinically based, but was frustrated in her ambition, and the opportunity was not available to her at Teacher's College for a long time. From the earliest time that she was associated with Teacher's College they had a programme in nurse midwifery, taught by people who were full-time workers at the local maternity centre. Virginia desperately wanted the same sort of thing for nurses in every clinical branch but her pleas did not make much impression for a long time.

A breakthrough occurred in the 1950s when a course started in paediatric nursing, which made it easier for teachers in other fields to insist on some clinical teaching. About that time a course in mental health nursing started and Virginia started teaching a medical and surgical nursing course. 'When that course was started, Frances Reiter worked with me, but she did not want to do the fieldwork and so I went with the students on the fieldwork. That course was so demanding that I had to give up the other courses that I had been teaching. I then began to devote my entire time to teaching these

49

advanced courses to the medical and surgical nursing graduates, some of whom had fifteen–twenty years' previous experience. That was one of the most satisfying things that I had done; although I suppose the introduction to the research technique was as useful to the profession as anything I did. I think the teaching of the medical and surgical nursing courses I did marked the turning point.'

It was a demanding course. Virginia and her students spent two whole days in hospitals in New York City caring for patients, for an unbroken semester. Virginia did all the fieldwork in the first year of the course but in the second year the numbers of students increased tremendously and an assistant came to work with her who was equally very much at home in the clinical programme. Lectures were minimal; the course was arranged entirely differently from any teaching programme at that time. It was almost entirely taught in clinical settings. As 'nursing a baby with pneumonia was nothing like nursing a middle-aged person, we taught about how you adapted care according to their age group. Another unit was about how you dealt with long-term illness and how you dealt with acute febrile disease, and how you protected yourself and other people from patients with communicable diseases. There were other units as well.'

Students then divided themselves up into groups, taking the responsibility for the discussion and development of the content of those different units, and presenting them to the class for discussion. While studying the units students were in the hospitals selecting patients that represented the problems they were discussing. Each student worked two days a week in hospital and chose up to three patients and planned their care, and worked with the staff at the hospital. Virginia 'had long believed that a working care plan of a patient was helpful because for a long time I had been going around on a voluntary basis taking care of patients, and the only way I knew what to do for that patient was to find out what had happened the day before. I realised that was not a very good guide because any number of emergencies could have arisen that would have not made out a typical day at all, and I realised that plan of care should be revised constantly as the patient got better.'

Virginia also began writing about planning nursing care and demonstrating how you did it, and showing how you involved the patients in the planning of their care. People began to see the sense of it, Virginia claims. Actually before she started teaching this course she took half a year off to do voluntary staff-nursing duties in New York Hospital 'to see whether I was still competent in giving beside care. I loved it, and I felt every day as excited as if I were going to the theatre.'

A lot of emphasis was placed during the course on the participation of the patient in the planning of care. Each of the graduate students was expected to hold a 'nursing clinic' in which everybody who had participated in the care of a particular patient was invited to come into a room with the patient, and any member of his/her family or friends, and discuss together what they had being doing. Each student reviewed the patient's history and tried to bring the patient into the conversation because it seemed to Virginia to be very rude to be talking about a person and to use language that they might not understand, so they tried to involve the patient throughout the session. The patient was encouraged to be very critical about what had been done. The students found this very hard at first but, in due course, they began to become much more sensitive towards the patient's needs. Virginia also wanted to demonstrate the need to involve the visiting nurses, who attended the patients when they went home from the hospital, but she never succeeded; the rules were too rigid on both sides to allow the students to go into the homes of the patients, much to her regret.

Initially Virginia had a problem to get the medical staff to co-operate in student education 'but it did not take too long'. She often brought appropriate material to the hospital for the students to read to save them time, and they did not hesitate, if the patient was all right, to sit down and study. One day a younger doctor complained about this and said there was a shortage of nurses. Virginia asked him if he realised that the young woman student was paying 80 cents an hour for the privilege of nursing this patient — paying to use the patient as a means of learning.

She thought that the medical staff should learn what they were doing so she asked to see the chief of that service and went to see him with one of the teaching supervisors. They were ushered into his room and the medical man — 'the big chief' — kept on looking at his mail, expecting Virginia to talk while he accomplished his work. Whereupon Virginia became very angry and said that it appeared that they had come at an inconvenient time. 'Perhaps you would like to set another time for us to come to talk to you when you are free to talk to us?' He dropped everything and he looked at Virginia and said, 'You are from the South, aren't you?' She said she was. 'He could see that I was angry and so he did give us an ear. I explained to him what we were doing and I think he was rather impressed because after that he never lost a chance when he saw me to ask how things were going.' After that episode Virginia 'felt as if we had got excellent co-operation from the medical services.' They began to participate in the inter-disciplinary conferences and Virginia believes they felt that they were beneficial. They helped in planning the care of the patients. 'I think we demonstrated the value of a team approach.'

Virginia says she did very little 'teaching'. She helped the students learn. Her schedule was hectic. Apart from the supervision of her students she spent many weekends in the medical library studying and very often ran into the students doing the same thing. She remembers one of the doctors saying, in a very patronising way: 'Oh, Miss Henderson, I see you get into the literature' — as if it was no place for a nurse!

Those years really made Virginia feel that she had accomplished something at last because her students began introducing her approach to care into their programmes. They often wrote to her to tell her how it was affecting their teaching and how much their students liked it.

Virginia believes her students acquired a great deal of confidence in presenting what they were studying to the whole class. They were encouraged to get experts in the field to come and give lectures before their presentations, and to discuss some of the problems involved, and the families of the patients were encouraged to come along to the classroom and work with the students on the presentation. The patients also eventually became convinced that the group was pretty willing for them to express a dissenting opinion. It was very free atmosphere and very constructive.

An advantage that they had at Teacher's College was that they had a nursing laboratory with all the equipment usually found in hospital utility rooms. The American Hospital Supply Company would literally give Virginia anything they manufactured. They sent equipment by the car load. The laboratory had moveable walls so that they could make any teaching area look like part of a ward, a private room in a hospital. The students enjoyed the way they could have different set-ups for their presentations. That kind of laboratory was a laboratory for teaching nursing situations without patients. That is controversial today and a lot of people say it should be abandoned, but Virginia thinks such a suggestion is absurd, not least because it was very hard to get the students into an appropriate clinical situation. It is too hard on the clinical teaching space to have everybody fighting to use it. She cannot see any objection to having something taught in a laboratory if it can simulate the clinical setting exactly. It is a convenience. It saves teaching time and it saves the infinite time needed in scheduling the use of the clinical teaching space. But she feels that the real strength of her teaching was that she was actually teaching in the clinical settings as well. 'That is exactly right, and any time that we felt that it would be better to teach in a clinical situation, and we could get the clinical space, we used it.'

The reason Virginia eventually left Teacher's College was because of a disagreement with the Dean (Miss McManus). It was a disagreement about the use of Virginia's time, as she felt pressure on her to give up her clinical work. She was never quite sure why Miss McManus wanted her to give it up because to Virginia it was obvious that it was the best thing that she had ever done. The Dean wanted Virginia to use her time to chair a new curriculum development group but she did not want to spend time working on the curriculum and struggling to get consensus, not least as she felt that she was demonstrating a new and effective kind of clinical teaching, which she would have had to have given up. 'That would have ruined it for me', says Virginia.

Virginia is happy that her students also became her disciples. Many became leaders. 'They went into many different things. I think they used

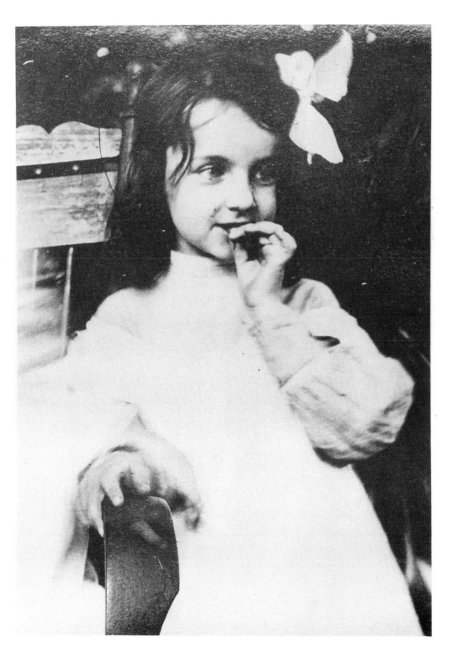

The young Virginia Henderson, 1903

Above: Bellevue – Virginia Henderson's childhood home

Below: Daniel Henderson (seated, centre) with members of the Siouan family of the Ponca tribe at the Smithsonian Institute, Washington DC

some of those methods that we used, because they were sold in it.'

Virginia was not able to win the argument with the Dean. She left partly for that reason and partly because she wanted to revise her nursing textbook, *Textbook of the Principles and Practice of Nursing*. The fourth edition had been co-authored in 1939 by Bertha Harmer and Virginia Henderson, but the fifth edition in 1955 was by Virginia alone.

Virginia had open conflict with Miss McManus because she felt that the course in medical and surgical nursing was obviously a success, not least because of the way the students responded. Students who were unhappy at having to do it in the beginning ended the most ardent supporters of the course. Virginia, therefore, considered it very arbitrary to be asked to give up what she thought was the 'cream' of the programme, i.e. working with patients and students in a clinical situation. Her salary when she left Teacher's College in 1948 was less than $5000 a year. Her assistant took over the course when she left.

After leaving the College, Virginia continued to live near the College — within a block of it, in the same apartment she had when teaching. At that time there was rent control and so she was paying about $100 a month for an extremely nice apartment. She was allowed to decorate it. It had a long room at the front; one end was the sitting room and the other the dining room. There was a kitchen and bedroom that opened into that room. It had very high ceilings. Then there was a hall room with a bathroom off it. At the back of the apartment there was a studio with a sitting room/bedroom, and that was where she had a piano. As she had to support herself while revising her textbook, she moved into the studio apartment at the back and rented the front part of the apartment, so practically the only expense she had was for food. Virginia intended to 'dig in, in that back room and write that revision of the book, but that did not happen.' Her tenant, Orielle Murphy, almost immediately proposed that they should share the use of the kitchen and that they should take meals together. Virginia also had a small income from the royalties from the fourth edition of her book.

About that time her cousin, Kitty Abbott Johnson, the wife of Joe Johnson (who was working at the United Nations) came to live in New York nearby to Virginia. Joe Johnson later took over the directorship of the Carnegie Foundation for International Peace based in New York City. Kitty was more like a sister to Virginia than a cousin, was very interested in what she was doing and was a 'wonderful influence' on the text. Virginia was 'writing this book for student and graduate nurses so I thought I ought to make the language understandable to any intelligent human being. Kitty read each chapter as I wrote it and if she did not understand what I was writing about, I changed it.'

Virginia spent five years working on the revision. She recalls that sometimes she became 'discouraged because my life, during those five years, consisted of going to work in the mornings and sitting down at my desk and staying there for as long as I could bear it, and I wasn't used to it. I got very depressed during that period because I had led such an active life.' Her older sister (Lucy) retired from teaching English around that time. She could type and she suggested that she would come and spend some time with Virginia and type the manuscript. Naturally, Virginia was delighted, and she came and typed it. Lucy and Kitty also read the proofs. Virginia recalls that her sister was very surprised to find that Virginia could write as well as she could. But Virginia Henderson is an expert at poking fun at her own skills and accomplishments! In her previous revision of Miss Harmer's textbook, Virginia did not alter very much 'but the second time that book became really my book.'

The American Hospital Supply Company sent a truck load of their latest equipment for Virginia to use in her pictures for the book. The Clay Adams Company furnished photographers. Virginia spent weeks up at the Columbia Presbyterian Hospital working in a temporarily vacant wing where she was permitted to photograph her illustrations of equipment and procedures. The hospital would not let her use their nurses as models in these pictures because at that time there was a prohibition against a nurse from their school of nursing working except with her cuffs right down to her wrists. As she had been very influenced by work with medical and surgical asepsis (and thought that nurses should not have long sleeves) and wanted to demonstrate good aseptic medical and surgical aseptic techniques, she had to get nurses who would roll up their sleeves or who would work in a gown. A person who manufactured nurses' uniforms sent a whole rack of them up to Virginia. That donor is in bed in some of the pictures in the book. A son of a grocer friend was also a subject in many of the pictures. Ironically, he was going to be a doctor but he was so disenchanted by the time he got through being a subject for all these things, that he gave up the idea!

Miss Hamlin, who was a Finnish nurse, was on a visit to the USA at the time and was asked if she would like to work with Virginia while she was taking these pictures. She agreed and her hands are in many of the pictures for that fifth edition (she did not want her face shown).

The illustrations for that book were outstanding, Virginia says, because they had skilled photographers and they had the use of the hospital wing. The Clay Adams Company who provided expert photographers sold the illustrations for the book as teaching aids. She also had expert people helping her to produce the book, including the publisher's editor (Barbara Russell). Barbara Russell and Virginia were allowed by the publishers to produce the book exactly the way they wanted it, which is exactly the opposite to what had happened when she was working on the previous edition. 'I have been told that book won a prize for just the looks of it', Virginia often says, with pride.

That five years of writing was a fruitful period for Virginia and made more tolerable by Orielle Murphy, who was a leading spirit in the Lincoln School for Children. She was a counsellor for students and an excellent educator. Very soon her friends became Virginia's friends and vice versa. Orielle only lived there for two or three years. When Lucy came to type the manuscript, she gave up the apartment.

Apart from visits to Canada during that five-year period for several quite long teaching periods and occasional lecturing or consultation work, Virginia devoted all her time to the book. She had a tremendous amount of reading to do in conection with it. She employed a young assistant and she and Virginia would go to a medical library regularly and get a stack of books 'and work all day very profitably'. It was unusual then to have well-researched nursing textbooks. Virginia still thinks her book is the most researched text that she has ever seen.

When the fifth edition of the book was published in 1955 it had one or two reviews in the journals in the United States that were laudatory, but Virginia does not remember any of them questioning the depth of the text until the next (sixth) edition came out in 1978. Virginia was troubled with the reviews of the sixth edition; she thought the reviews took a very limited view of the nurse's function. One questioned the reproduction of a genetic report in the textbook, saying what did nurses have to do with genetics and suggesting that nurses should not be counsellors for people on genetic problems. The review that really pleased Virginia and one that had an effect on her subsequent work, and, in her view, on the way people regarded her work, was a review in 1956 by Bethina Bennet, OBE, a British nurse. Her review was so long that it was put in three issues of the *Nursing Mirror*. In Virginia's view the review showed that Bethina had really read the book. Mrs Bennet thought the book was, to some extent, revolutionary in its scope. At that time she was Chairman of the Professional Services' Committee of the International Council of Nurses and she saw the possibilities of putting the essence of that book into a very small pamphlet that could be translated by member countries of the ICN. Virginia was asked to write the pamphlet and ICN published it but it was not attributed to Virginia in its first printing. That was rectified in subsequent reprints. The pamphlet is now published in about twenty-five languages. Virginia receives no royalties for that publication but she is glad to think that she has helped the ICN by providing a source of income for it since its first publication in 1960 under the title *Basic Principles of Nursing Care*. Virginia has no regrets about the ICN publication at all. She says, 'I was trying to say to people that this is the way I nurse. I did not think of it as a philosophy or a definition of nursing.' But while few, if any, have disagreed fundamentally with her ICN statement as published, Virginia often says in view of her own team concept, 'The thing that I marvel at is that nobody has said, "Well, that is what other health workers do also." I believe that doctors and nurses are overlapping workers.'

Something that troubles Virginia tremendously is whether her textbook ('*The Principles and Practice of Nursing*') will ever appear in a seventh edition, not least because of the present preoccupation with the 'nursing process' (assessing, planning, implementing and evaluating care), both by nurses and nursing publishers. 'Now, I deal in this book with the way I think that concept developed. I give a historical perspective on it', she points out, 'but I do not promote it as an approach. I suppose I more or less dismiss it by saying it is a problem-solving process, which applies to any occupation's work that approaches the work as if it is a series of problems.' As Virginia argues, 'in many papers that I have written I don't think nursing is just a series of problems. To me it is a distortion of our work rather than a way of explaining the most desirable approach to it. If you are going to talk about the nursing process you have to talk about the medical and social processes.' While the nursing process is one of a number of *models* of nursing, Virginia Henderson has provided us with a *definition* of nursing.

While Virginia concedes that the 'nursing process' seems to have given a great many nurses more confidence in the value of their work, especially in the USA, she believes the problem-solving process, if applicable to nursing, is applicable to all the other health professions. She believes that nursing is as complex as work can be which involves your head, your heart and your hands. She does not think it is just a problem-solving process, nor does she believe nurses have enhanced the status of this service by calling it the 'nursing process'.

Virginia is convinced that her book would have received greater promotion and sales if she had appeared more committed to the 'nursing process' but principles are more important to her than profits.

A nice thing about this book happened to her in the early 1980s when a graduate nursing student, named David Evans, entered the Yale University School of Nursing. When he first started using the book he came down and talked to Virginia. He could not understand why people felt sorry for you if you were a nurse. He could not see anything that was arduous or distasteful, and he believed nursing was more like making love. He told Virginia at his graduation ceremony that he had written an article about her that was going to be published. He said it was really about her book. He had taught English before taking nursing courses and so he was very aware of the way the book was written. He said very nice things about the style of the book. The whole article was about what effect, if adopted and used, this book would have on nursing. He thought that it hit the nail on the head, because it was a description of good practice in nursing. It would have been a tremendous boost for the book if everybody had read his article, Virginia argues. David Evans became a paediatric nurse practitioner in Oklahoma. In Virginia's view 'he is the only person I have thought of as a possible editor for the revision of this text because he is so in sympathy with it. I don't know whether he will do it or not.' Time will tell.

CHAPTER 8

The Nursing Index
Project at Yale

In 1953, Leo Simmonds, a sociologist, approached Virginia and asked if she would be interested in working on a survey and assessment of nursing research. He was, at that time, working with a Dr Wolf at New York Hospital, which was connected with Cornell University. He had interviewed many nurses in connection with the work he was doing in patient care with Dr Wolf, including a former student of Virginia's when she was at Teacher's College. She suggested to Leo Simmonds that if he was looking for a nurse to help him in his research, Virginia would be a good person to ask.

Leo approached Virginia before she had finished the revision of her textbook. She told him she would work with him as soon as she had finished the revision but she could not, at that moment, give full time to anything else. However, while awaiting publication of the book, she started to work with him and a sociologist from the University of Pennsylvania, Ray Abrams. They used to come and meet at her apartment in New York City and prepare plans. Virginia did not think twice about accepting their offer because she felt it sounded tremendously interesting.

The first summer that she was employed she came and lived in a house with Ray Abrams and a woman sociology student (but she did not stay on the project for any length of time). The sociologists and Virginia worked on how they were going to tackle the survey of nursing research. After that summer when Virginia went to Yale University, Leo and she, together with a secretary, were the only workers left on the project. The initial project was funded through the Yale University School of Nursing. The advisory Committee membership included Dean Bixler of Yale Nursing School, and a member of the public health department, but Virginia does not recall them ever being much help.

Virginia was given the title of Research Associate on the faculty of the School of Nursing. The proposal for the study came from a National Service Committee, set up after the Second World War, made up of nurses and others, including physicians and social scientists. The committee discovered that there was no control over nursing literature and that it was contained in very few libraries. The committee wanted a study made to list all the things that they wanted as a basis for action. They wanted to discover where the books which they needed were. This involved documenting what had been done and, in due course, recommending how in the future things could be reported and publicised.

It was understandable to seek Virginia's help, for she had been saying for years that what was needed more than anything in nursing was an index of nursing literature. She saw in it a realisation of a long-held dream, while Leo saw in it something that had to be planned from scratch! They asked for a grant for something like $32,000 from the US Public Health Service, but Virginia hastens to point out that she never had anything to do with the management of the budget!

Leo told Virginia that since they had no index file they could only find out about things from librarians; fieldwork was therefore necessary. As Leo could not give up his teaching work at Yale, Virginia had to do the fieldwork; fortunately, that appealed to her very much. 'In fact', she says, 'I think it is something that I will always be grateful for because it was a liberal education and I went to about three-quarters of the States and met key people in most of the States, like the deans of the nursing schools and medical schools, groups of staff nurses and student nurses.' It involved meeting people who had done any research in the field of nursing wherever she went. In some of the colder States she encountered temperatures below zero that she had never encountered before.

The project entailed Virginia commuting to Yale for five days a week from her apartment in New York but she became rather tired of that and before very long she rented a guest room in a friend's house in New Haven. This friend travelled a lot and liked staying in Mexico for two months in the winter, when Virginia had her apartment all to herself.

Leo Simmonds had two offices in the Graduate School of Sociology at Yale. His secretary and Virginia shared one room and he had the other and it was very comfortable working there. Virginia found the faculty at the Graduate School very interesting. They used to have tea every afternoon. She was soon involved in the tea arrangements and felt very much a hostess at that tea and met a great variety of interesting people. In particular she met the people who were working on the Dead Sea Scrolls. She remembers one theologian who said something to her that she has never forgotten: 'Miss Henderson, don't you realise there is no such thing as a fact. The fact is something that you believe to be true.' They used to have many productive arguments on new slants on all kinds of questions.

Virginia was all for making a systematic search of the literature but they did not have time to make as thorough a search as she would have wished. At the time, the *Index Medicus* was indexing only three or four nursing journals and, therefore, to search the nursing journals was quite a task. As she felt that the articles in *Index Medicus* were specially selected, she had to discover which nursing journals were published and look at them all. They made no attempt to use any language other than English but, even so, it was a formidable task to look at several hundred nursing journals from all over the world.

Later they decided to add monographic material too, that, of course, increased the work. They had to make a classification system — later published in a book. The fieldwork and travelling were expensive but Virginia tried to make it as reasonable as possible by travelling at night, thus eliminating a lot of hotel bills. She usually communicated with the deans in the large nursing schools in the areas she planned to visit in the hope that they knew the people they wished to talk to.

Leo went with Virginia on the first trip to demonstrate the interviewing technique that he thought worked and to give her an idea of the people who were important to talk to. They went to Cleveland University, Ohio, and spoke to the President of the University, the Dean of the Medical School and the Dean of Public Health. Virginia soon learnt that the conversation got round to the interests of the person they were interviewing so she learnt a great deal about medical education. 'Before I knew it,' she recalls, 'the Dean of the Medical School would say that problem is not unique to nursing, we have that in medical school, and then he would talk about the escape from the bedside amongst doctors that took them away from medical practice. Through that fieldwork I learnt what was going on, way beyond the confines of nursing agencies and their field of practice.'

Those field trips often lasted for several months so that Virginia could make the best use of the funds. The main purpose of the trips was to present people with three questions relating to research they thought would be useful for a survey of research by nurses, or research that had affected nursing. The questions were:

What have you done, if any?
What do you know that we should know about?
If you had resources, what research would you do?

During the 1950s (when the survey started) there was growing interest about nursing research in the USA. There had been an exposé of conditions in American mental hospitals and that had led to establishing Mental Health Commissions in practically every State. There were always one or two nurses on these commissions and they began to hear that the improvement of psychiatric nursing, like all nursing, depended upon identifying problems and taking analytical approaches, and setting up remedial programmes that took the problems into consideration. Hence the focus on nursing research. As a result, Virginia points out that 'If you asked people's opinion on what was needed they were very likely to mention a survey of this or that, but you could count on them saying that you needed a definition of nursing, because the American Nurses' Foundation had voiced this opinion.'

During the 1950s at least seventeen major surveys were made in the USA

59

in order to arrive at a definition of nursing. One important study that was done in California in more than one hospital found that nurses were engaged in more than 500 specific tasks, overlapping their functions with other occupational groups. It was found, in small hospitals, that everybody went home at seven o'clock at night, except nurses. So, if a drug had to be prepared there were no pharmacists and the night superintendent had to do it whether she knew how to do it or not. The overlapping of the nurse's work in rural areas was startling.

In those early years a group of doctors asked Virginia to come down and look at what nurses were doing in a Pennsylvania hospital. She did not realise that the nurses had nothing to do with her invitation. The doctors hoped Virginia would help to find out what was wrong with what nurses were doing and tell them so that they would correct it. She went, pretty naively, to that hospital, she admits. She found that the doctors' grievance was really that the board of directors were working through the nurse administrator of the hospital rather than coming to the medical board with problems. They felt that they were being neglected.

Virginia discovered the nursing staff were, in fact, running that hospital. The nurses also had many complaints against the physicians. For instance, Wednesday afternoon was the physicians' time for golf. It was almost impossible to get a physician on that day if a patient needed one. The nurses were doing many tasks in that rural hospital which were more appropriate to a pharmacist or doctor. At the end of the visit Virginia had accumulated a good deal of data and had dinner with five or six doctors of the medical board who wanted her to tell them what was wrong with nursing. But instead she 'told them that when they asked me to come down I did not realise that this was a group of doctors asking me to find out what was wrong with the nursing personnel. I said, "How would any of you like it if you found that a nurse had come down to find out what was wrong with the medical running of this place?" I added "Incidentally, I have discovered a good deal that people think is wrong with the performance of the medical personnel!"'

They were very nice about it. Virginia remembers one of them saying he would never again treat nurses in the way he had been treating them. She was very relieved that her frankness was not distasteful to them and suggested that they formed an inter-disciplinary body and put some citizens on it and find out how to improve the hospital. She told them to start relieving nurses of the necessity of going into the pharmacy and making up drugs.

In the survey work Virginia found that the reported research concentrated largely on the nurse and on her work so that when she was asked to write an editorial for *Nursing Research* she wrote a brief editorial entitled 'Nursing Research – When?' That was because she was concerned that research findings focused on the nurse as a worker rather than the effect of her work on the patient. Clinically focused research was minimal, she discovered.

When she was not doing field work, Virginia was studying the literature. First, she read everything that was in the Yale library and then made trips to libraries in New York, Washington and any other library she could. One of the things they decided to do was to annotate all the documents and dissertations written by nurses. In the report they sent to the US Public Health Service at the end of the 1950s, fewer than 200 dissertations were identified as written by nurses, dating from about 1930. It was also perfectly obvious that the people who were helping nurses with their dissertations were educators, social scientists and almost never medical practitioners interested in research. The whole file of research reports that they began to build up contained much more research in nurse education than anything else. It more than equalled all the other research.

The work identified some centres where research had been done by students when getting their Master's degree or doctorate. The Catholic University in Washington DC was a conspicuous example of one institution that was committed to research. Virginia learnt a lot about the research resources and research interests in nursing in the USA. There were many pretty unsophisticated responses to their questions, Virginia says.

There was precious little assessment of the importance of nursing education in patient care in spite of the large amount of nursing education research. There were studies of wastage — reasons for dropping out of programmes. She was amazed at how little of the research was, like medical research, focused on clinical activities. It just seemed to be what nurses felt they could study. Virginia concluded that the members of the faculties who knew anything at all about how to do research were likely to be the social scientists. Sociologists, she says, dominated the nursing research that was being done because they were nearly always the people on the faculty who were in charge of research. It was rare to have nurses supervising nursing research and in the 1950s there were so few nurses with Doctor's degrees.

They published fifty copies of the kind of report that the US Public Health Service required. They had a difficult time getting that study financed until they had enough data to justify a description, and Leo must have looked for a source beyond the US Public Health Service. Virginia thinks he diverted some of his grants that he had got from other sources to help pay her salary; that first grant of $32,000 did not cover the expenses. After the Public Health Service received the copies of the report they agreed to finance the next stage of the study.

Leo left to go to Teacher's College to direct the research programmes within the department of nursing. He left before they got the report ready for general publication and they found the only way to do it was for him to take certain jobs and Virginia to take the others. The book was in due course a compilation of sections written by both of them individually.

Leo left Yale around 1959 and at that time Florence Wald was appointed Dean of the Yale School of Nursing and was very interested in the survey because she had spent a number of years doing medical research. (It was the start of a lifelong friendship between Florence and Virginia.) She saw that Virginia had a resource there that should be made available to everybody and talked to Virginia about the possibility of getting a grant that would enable her to get that file ready for publication. She did not think that effort should be lost.

Virginia then became Director of the Nursing Studies Index Project at a salary of not much more than $6000 or $7000 a year. She finally got a grant for $30,000 and moved from the Graduate School office to another one in the Nursing School, where she quickly began to feel very much part of the School and went to the faculty meetings. She then turned her attentions to setting up an advisory committee for this new project.

The advisory committee consisted of experts including a publisher who had a good list of publications in the health field and a librarian from Yale. Leo Simmonds was also on it. They had someone from the *American Journal of Nursing* and the editor of the *Nursing Research Journal*. Someone from the *Index Medicus* was also on the committee. In addition, a co-ordinating committee of twelve was appointed.

After the first meeting of the co-ordinating committee, they voted to establish themselves as an Inter-agency Council on Library Resources for nursing. That body still meets twice a year and it now represents about twenty different agencies. Virginia considers that one of her lasting contributions made to nursing. The advisory committee consisted of people who would be most helpful in deciding what they were going to do with the big file of cards.

The Inter-Agency Council not only represented people in the USA but also a librarian from Canada was asked to come because Canadian nurses have an excellent library, comparable to that at the Royal College of Nursing. There was a feeling among those who went to the meeting that nurses had access to the medical libraries where they worked. A survey of practices in those hospitals demonstrated that nurses did not feel welcome in them and there were certain hours of the day when they could not have access to them. It was also noted that the *American Journal of Nursing* library was an editorial library that was there to serve the editors of the journals and was not set up to be used as a national resource for nurses. They also found that nurses were not contributing to the support of the resources at the National Library of Nursing in Bethesda.

In due course a regional body on library resources for nursing was formed. It still meets once a year in Durham, New Hampshire. Virginia thinks 'It has improved the library resources for nurses in New England. I would like to think that these regional meetings will be set up all over the country.' They agreed two things when funds were received: that they make this collection of cards available to the public, and also to record the surveying process for the benefit of the nursing profession.

At the first meeting of the co-ordinating body, Virginia and a librarian presented a recommendation that the national nursing organisations should promote the creation of a national nursing index or an international index that would continue the work that they were then doing at Yale. Interestingly enough, that motion was defeated. It was agreed that nurses had the *Index Medicus*, the hospital index, the reader's guide and the index to the general literature, and that they did not need a nursing index. The next time they met, Virginia and her colleague made the same proposal, showing them how inadequately nursing literature was indexed in the existing indexes. It was not defeated. A librarian, who was also a nurse, was asked to make a survey, and produced a report that supported Virginia's contention that nursing was not served adequately by the existing indexes. That is when she really got started on indexing the nursing literature.

In about 1966 the first volume of the *International Nursing Index* was published. This included the indexing of all the literature around the world that she had access to. Thereafter they produced the retrospective index volume by volume, because it was the only way that they could continue to get support for it. The project lasted eleven years and it was impossible to persuade the people who were financing it that it was important unless they could see what was being attempted — and accomplished.

This was particularly important because on the Inter-Agency Council major nursing organisations were represented and there was a certain amount of tension between the factions that believed in the status quo, and the people who were fighting for change. 'You can guess what side I was on,' Virginia says, 'because I thought the status quo was very inadequate.'

During that period Virginia went to England on a pleasure trip and asked the office of the Royal College of Nursing (RCN) to set up a meeting for her with British people who would be interested in her project, 'because,' she suggests, 'the New York Public Health Service was absolutely sick of us. They had been funding us for five years and they hadn't seen any results, and thought that by that time we should have produced some publication to show what we had been doing with their money.'

At the RCN, Virginia found a delightful group who had been invited to come and talk to her, 'but it was a tea-party. It was not set up at all as a business meeting.' They said quite frankly to her that they did not know what an index was. Nobody had used an index to the literature so she did not even get to the first stage in persuading them that they needed one! The group consisted of a number of RCN officers and other nurses and a representative of one of the British publishing houses. She thinks that she would have needed to have had an educational seminar at that meeting to get their support, because they could not envisage what she was talking about. She thinks that they were relatively satisfied with the status quo.

Virginia thinks the rather negative responses to her project were unfortunate as it would have been very appropriate for it to be an international project. With regret she feels she 'got far too little understanding and certainly no promise of financial support from that meeting in England.' However, when she was back home again she did persuade the Public Health Service to continue to support them until the last two or three years of the project. By that time their patience and understanding were worn out, she says. The National Library of Medicine supported the last few years of the work on the index — thanks to the support of a former colleague from the US Surgeon General's office.

A Canadian librarian, named James Kirk, who worked with Virginia on the project for nearly all the eleven years, read more sources and made more annotations than anybody on that team except Virginia. He was very quick and intelligent and wrote very good annotations, and could wade through a pile of work that very few other people would have been willing to undertake.

At staff meetings, Virginia insisted on everybody involved in the work sitting around the table and becoming familiarised with every aspect of that work, including the difficulty they were having in getting funds. She made everyone share the burden of that work, but as it was not the way they were accustomed to working, they hated those meetings. They did not share Virginia's democratic feelings. All the workers were asked to come to the meetings of the advisory committee as Virginia wanted everybody working on that project to share the success, or the failure, of it. She remembers one occasion when a librarian was so rude to a secretary that they had to stop the meeting. The librarian was objecting to the way the staff meeting was being taken. She had many difficulties to combat with librarians. She asked one librarian how the library operated and was told that she did not concern herself with the details because she considered herself an administrator. Before the project was completed they had had at least eleven librarians working on it, because they came and left. Virginia believes, 'They did not like reading and doing the annotations, they wanted to edit.' But Virginia found reading those publications a thorough education. 'I know a great deal about how nursing has evolved and what its status is. I think I know more about nursing literature than any nurse in this country,' she claims, convincingly.

The money from the National Library of Medicine lasted up to the end of that project.

Virginia cannot remember a review of the *Index*. Nor can she remember any enthusiastic backing from any members of the nursing profession for the work that she had been doing. She had trouble getting a publisher because libraries, and not the individual, would be the purchasers. It was a 'prestige item' for a publisher, i.e. something they would not make money on. However, Virginia managed to get the *Index* published because one of the nurse administrators at Yale told her to go to the publisher she wanted and ask them how much money they wanted to publish it. It worked! The American publishers J B Lippincott said they would do it if she would pay a certain percentage of their losses on publishing. So she then went to the American Nursing Foundation that had been set up to fund research and asked them if they would be willing to guarantee a percentage of the publisher's losses. As far as she knows, they never asked for any money. They published it. 'One of the happiest things was when they brought the new published volume to me personally to New York,' Virginia recalls. But she is still terribly disappointed that the nursing profession has not developed habits of scholarship. She often sees dissertations that suggest that scholarship is non-existent. They don't seem to use the *Nursing Index* as a resource. 'I am disappointed,' she says, 'that the nursing profession has adopted this attitude that anything published before 1970 isn't useful. What makes me happy, however, is that the *International Nursing Index* is still being published.' Virginia believes her work is unique as an annotated index of books and journal articles is rare.

Virginia continually regrets that there are very few professions, including nursing, that have a course of instruction for the students in finding out what is in print. The only professional curriculum where she found that included was in the course for lawyers in one of the American universities.

As Virginia was very much part of the Yale faculty she was able to influence the way they taught their students in terms of searching the literature. She began by giving the students of the Yale School an introduction to the use of the literature that she had brought to classes. She would fill several tables with books as 'library tools', describing them and indicating the use that could be made of them. The faculty began to realise that maybe the students knew more about this than they, the members, did, she says. Eventually 'they then asked me to do it for the faculty. I had a very good response.'

Subsequently the *American Journal of Nursing* company took over the project but, initially, they were a little resistant to the idea of an index! The representative of that company voted against the proposal for an index the first time it was put to the Inter-Agency Council by Virginia. But from the outset they saw themselves as collaborators and ever since they have wanted to sponsor the index and control of the sales of it. As Virginia points out, few people have the satisfaction of seeing something that they have triggered off continuing for ever. 'It is a tremendous satisfaction to me even though I used to be teased for my enthusiasm for getting all the control of our literature.' But she also believes nurses should refer to the complementary indexes, e.g. *Index Medicus*, and one published by the Seventh Day Adventist Hospital, California. 'I am very much against nurses sticking only to what has been written by and for nurses', is her constant belief, as 'our work overlaps with that of the physicians.'

65

Having an office next door to Florence Wald made Virginia feel very much included in and part of the things that were happening at the Yale School. Florence made Virginia chairman of a committee that worked on the relationship between the School of Nursing, the School of Medicine, the Hospital, and the Graduate School, and there were very interesting people on the committee.

Virginia felt very much involved in what was happening at Yale. While she was there the 'nursing process' evolved and almost always dominated faculty meetings. At that time, Robert Leonard was a tutor in research in the School. He helped both the faculty and students conduct studies. All the students attempting to get a Master's degree had to produce research of some sort. Ida Orlando, research fellow at Yale School of Nursing, was the leader in the study of the nursing process.

At Yale they were sure that they did not know enough about what the patient was thinking to give the best possible care; the communications were not adequate. So the faculty regularly talked about perceptions, thoughts and feelings, because it was a great concern to Ida Orlando and the other people associated with her. They had at that time two philosophers on the faculty – Professor Dickoff and Patricia James, who later married. They were helping the Yale faculty to establish nursing on a sound philosophical basis and accompanied the nurses on the floor as observers. The faculty meetings were stoney, but also very productive, Virginia recalls.

Although it was fruitful, she thinks that undue emphasis was put on the subject of the nursing process — how you taught it, how you used it — but it was still not 'all intrusive as it has since become'. Ida Orlando's work led to the publication of two books (*The Dynamic Nurse–Patient Relationship: Function, Process and Principles* in 1961 and *The Discipline and Teaching of Nursing Process: An Evaluative Study* in 1972, both published by Putnam of New York) and much of her work was incorporated in a publication by the nurse-midwife on that faculty, who later wrote a book on perceptions, thoughts and feelings, and the struggle to open channels of communication between the nurse and the patient. It was an absorbing book, in Virginia's view, because before that time nurses were afraid to talk to patients for fear that they would transgress the rules made for nurses as to what they could and could not say. They could not tell the patients if they knew what was wrong with them: medical diagnosis had to be conveyed by the doctor. Nurses were afraid of invading the doctor's territory. 'At that time nurses were just groping for a way of finding their territory', in Virginia's view.

The ethos at Yale School of Nursing created a tremendous impetus towards getting the role of the nurse more clearly defined, and to formulate descriptions of it that would help people.

Ida Orlando was a psychiatric nurse and Virginia supposes the psychiatric nurses at that time were influenced by the work of a psychiatrist named Laing. In Virginia's view, Laing was the exponent of the theory that you revealed yourself to the patient if you wanted the patient to reveal himself or herself to you. Ida Orlando shocked her very much one day by saying that she did not hesitate to say to a patient: 'You make me furious!' That is the last thing that Virginia would say to a patient. If they did make her furious she kept it to herself. There was a great dominance of psychiatric nurses at Yale at that time. Florence Wald was one. The school also prepared many nurses at the time for psychiatric specialisation, so it was quite a dominant group, and, inevitably, Virginia became very involved in this movement in the faculty.

Florence Wald, former Dean of the Yale University School of Nursing, wrote the foreword to the *Nursing Studies Index* and she said:

'The publication of this *Index* of literature on nursing may one day signify a turning point to historians who are studying the development of our profession. Those of us who attempted a search of nursing literature before a comprehensive index was listed will appreciate its value especially. We know what it meant to search the journals year by year, and in contrast how simple the task has now become when annotations of the significant aspects of all the literature in English are in a few volumes.

'The work has a special significance to the people who witnessed the construction of the *Index*. During these past three years the indexing staff had an office adjacent to mine. I know what long hours they kept, how willing they were to abandon one approach if someone found a better one, how they persevered to finish the *Index* in the shortest possible time, how much effort each one of the staff made to maintain a sense of proportion in the face of an assignment which made a constant demand for meticulousness. Miss Henderson gives well-deserved credit to the staff who worked with her; only modesty could prevent her from delineating her own role. It is doubtful if the project could have been undertaken without her.

'When the Yale School of Nursing first decided to undertake the project they encountered little difficulty in finding financial support but the key was to find the director for it who had the professional background of editorial skill. Serendipity played an important part in that Miss Henderson was available at that very time.

'This Foreword is dedicated to the unique and timely set of circumstances which permitted the *Index* to come about.'

CHAPTER 9
Theories, Models, Concepts

The 'modern' movement of concepts, models and theories is an 'old' story really, in Virginia's view; even when she was a student at Teacher's College, educational *theory* was talked about and courses arranged around it. So it is not a new idea that people want to establish a framework, with various names, to clarify their own thinking, and to explain to other people the reasoning behind their actions. But Virginia's feelings are clear when she says: 'I think it is a little bit foolish to oppose this. I don't believe that I am thought of as a person who has given undue emphasis to this because I think more often than not that I am impatient with the amount of time that we are devoting to it, and the number of people who are writing about it, and seeming to me to complicate the question. So much has been written that is either incomprehensible — you don't know what the people are talking about — or it is not vivid enough to enable you to remember it.' Virginia often fears that those views of hers, often expressed, have alienated some people in the nursing profession. But she has seen 'these things come and go.' It does not seem to her that the nature of nursing has changed to such an extent that it justifies these 'fashions' in nursing, that are fashionable one day and discarded the next. She concedes she may be completely mistaken in her reactions, but she is more interested in substance than in form.

When Virginia was part of a team at Teacher's College working on the revision of 'The Curriculum Guide' in 1937, the new edition was 'liberalised'. Isabel Stewart (head of nursing at Teacher's College) was really the prime mover on the review group. She wrote in the Introduction to this Guide that she thought it should be the *philosophy* of nursing. Interestingly enough, she used the same word that Sister Calista Roy now uses, which is *adaptation*. The idea was that the nurse must adapt the nursing care to the needs of the patient. Some people have wondered, says Virginia, with tongue in cheek, whether the patient didn't also have to adapt to the nurse! That idea of clarifying your philosophy of nursing, Virginia is sure, was useful in its day. Virginia feels she has much in common with the physician, Dr Edmund Pellegrino, former Dean of the New York State Health Science Centre Medical School at Stony Brook, New York, USA; he, as she does, often stressed the close working relationship between nurse and doctor. It is not surprising, therefore, that Virginia's philosophy of nursing is easily embraced into a philosophy of health care — carried out by a team of interdependent individuals. Pellegrino's views are explored in *A Philosophical Basis of Medical Practice: Toward a Philosophy and Ethic of the Healing Professions*, co-authored by D C Thomasma and published in 1981 by Oxford University Press.

Virginia recalls that in the 1950s the American Nursing Foundation was established to grand funds for research, to promote research, and, in some cases, to conduct research. One well-known social science researcher was Esther Lucille Brown; although not a nurse, she was funded to study nursing and set up a number of conferences. At one of those conferences, early in the '50s, Virginia said they ought to have a group studying a definition of nursing, to study what the *unique* function was. She has never thought that you could separate the functions of the nurse and the physician because she has believed, ever since she did public health nursing, that the nurse is often 'the family physician to the poor families' in the USA. There are geographical areas that are under-served by physicians, and better served by the nurses, she argues. This is where the nurse is functioning as a physician.

Virginia often argues that the distinction between the nurse and the doctor seems to be pretty absurd considering what is going on in different parts of the world. In the USA they have three to five times as many nurses as doctors compared with nurses in India, where the doctors are more numerous than nurses. 'It is absurd to think of our functions as the same in those two places', she points out. Furthermore, she argues, that if there are a lot of therapists, social workers and others available to a country, you cut the pie accordingly. It has never been an idea of Virginia's that you put a rigid boundary around the practices of professional workers.

'In my experience we first worried about our philosophy in nursing and we then turned our attention to trying to define our function in doing it, and I think I was the prime mover in that effort to define nursing. One reason why I was vocal on that subject was because by that time I had revised the textbook written by Miss Harmer. I realised then that if I was going to talk about nursing, I had to tell the reading public what I thought nursing was. Also I was teaching courses at Teacher's College, where it seemed to me to be reasonable to expect me to say, when I talked about teaching the courses, what the primary function of the nurse was. We ought to be able to tell the public about the thing that we perhaps do best, that we can do better than anyone else because we give more attention to it. I was one of the group who worked on stating the definition of the primary function of the nurse.'

Her confirmed view is that nursing is doing for others what they would do for themselves if they had the strength, will and the knowledge; and also that the nurse helps the patient to carry out the plan of therapy prescribed by the physician. She admits to an aversion to the words 'doctor's orders' — as there is a connotation in the word 'orders' that is associated with the military in her mind. She does not like to be ordered to do things because it implies that she has no choice. While recognising that prescribing for a patient is the role of a physician, she also thinks a patient is more than justified in disapproving of that prescription, if he wishes, as there are too many unused medications in the medicine cabinets. The doctor can order it but he cannot force that person to take it, in her view. Nor should nurses force patients to take medical prescriptions or care when that patient is convinced that it is wrong and is resisting it, she argues. Her conviction is that 'the function of the nurse is to help the patient. It is not the function of the nurse to carry out the doctor's orders, because I think sometimes it is the function of the nurse to resist an arbitrary order that she cannot believe in if she thinks it is going to be harmful to the patient. It is the nurse's function to help rehabilitate the patients, making them self-sufficient as soon as possible.'

Virginia thinks what happened in the '50s in the USA was quite significant. People paid a lot of attention to the studies that Esther Lucille Brown made on the profession of nursing. She has been a great influence on American nursing.

When an amount of money was available at the end of the 1950s for the study of nursing, seventeen different studies were done in different parts of the USA and summarised by another social scientist, Everett Hughes. About 500 activities were identified in hospital nursing staff alone. Details of these were published by the Californian State Nurses' Association in 1953 in *Nursing Practice in California Hospitals: A Report Based on a Study of Actual Practice in Forty California Hospitals*. These studies were begun with the assumption that there might be a more accurate definition of nursing obtained if it were known exactly what the nurses were doing. Many of these studies were activity analyses — an attempt was made to study nursing in all the settings in which they functioned. The largest study was done in California. What sticks in Virginia's mind was that nurses were identified as performing something like 500 different tasks. 'It was quite obvious that the function of the nurse was very diverse,' she recalls, 'nurses did what nobody else either wanted to do or was not available to do. They were more or less a jack of all trades and master of none. It was quite disturbing to the profession to find out how nurses were used for anything that nobody else wanted to do.' People then began to think that perhaps that was a good thing. Maybe it was very necessary for the welfare of the person being served. Maybe it was a good thing if nurses did not refuse to do anything. There were many reactions: some favourable and some unfavourable.

As one of the assumptions at the time was that nursing was what nurses do — so nurses wanted to know what nurses did. But, as Virginia recalls, they did not get a very satisfactory answer because that effort to define nursing was replaced by an effort to reassure nurses that what they were doing was the bona fide work of the profession; then followed a big effort to identify the independent role of the nurse. 'Ever since then we have been trying to show that we have an independent role and can function without a physician', Virginia suggests.

As doctors were prescribing *nursing* care in the USA, American nurses gave a big push to identify what they could do without the doctor in attendance. 'It is hard to understand how that developed in this country when we don't find similar practices in England', Virginia opines.

The irony and paradox are made explicit by Virginia: 'After 1950 the nurses wanted to know what they could do. The physicians still defend their right to diagnose and treat, which is just as absurd as us saying that nobody can nurse except ourselves. I think the populus should get the help they need and if there are not enough professionals to do it, they will have to get the best person they can to do it. They can't make any laws to prevent people from diagnosing and treating themselves. I do it all the time!' But what is the relevance of all this to theory, models, concepts? Well, in the '50s something happened; the social scientists' work informed nurses that they were all right as far as practical work was concerned but they could not conceptualise. That view gave American nurses a terrific inferiority complex, Virginia believes, because they were very much oppressed with this dictum of the social scientists who suggested that nurses were just *practical* people! They suggested that nurses had not given much thought or attention to a philosophy or theory of nursing.

In fairness, Virginia thinks the social scientists recognised that nurses believed there was a scientific basis for practice, but that nurses had given little thought to it. For her part, Virginia finds philosophy to have an unlimited scope and has no boundaries to it. She is impatient with the time nurses have devoted to philosophy. She wishes that 'some of these people who are writing all this philosophy would demonstrate their ability and knowledge of nursing. I wish at least they were part-time practitioners.'

Citing a review of the literature on the nursing process, commissioned by the Nursing Division, Department of Health, England, in the 1980s, Virginia says the conclusions were exactly what hers would be: that there has been no evidence that the use of the nursing process has improved the nursing service. It may have raised professional self-esteem and that may have given nurses more confidence; but there is no evidence of the patient getting better faster because the nursing process has been used.

Virginia's stance is certainly not anti-intellectual. Far from it. She desperately wants nurses to take a much more aggressive stand on their interpretation of the needs of the patient, not least because the nurse is with the patient so much more than the doctors. Nine times out of ten, she believes, a well-prepared nurse could prescribe a more effective regimen for the patient than the doctor can possibly do, because he is with the patient for such a short time. She synthesises her views like this: 'I believe that nurses are prepared to take a much more important role in the care of the patient than they are now doing. I think that if a nurse is making one diagnosis and the doctor another, they never seem to meet to discuss it. I think it is doing the patient more harm than good. I think it is taking up a great deal of time in writing with this nursing process, and the nurse could spend it more effectively if she was with the patient.' She confirms this view by recalling a visit to a hospital in Manchester, England, a few years ago. Her observation of their use of the nursing process was on a unit for elderly patients who were there on average for over a month, whereas the average stay for patients in most US hospitals is less than five or six days, she points out. Indeed, she feels it is a scandal in the USA the way the patients are sent back home too soon because, if they stay for a shorter time than the Diagnosis Related Group (DRG) allows payment, the hospital gains money. Now unless the nursing process is useful to the practising nurse, in Virginia's judgment, it cannot be promoted as a way to nurse people. It is just like the case-study method that students used years ago, she says. She concedes that using the nursing process may be a useful student exercise and may help a student to learn something but, in her view, as far as she knows, the nursing process as described in print has not been demonstrated as a way the graduate nurse practises. It still seems to her to be something you teach other people! Nursing process records she has seen tend to overemphasise the social aspects and underemphasise the biomedical aspects of health, she says, with regret. For instance, there is often no indication in the records that the drugs used for the patients have been studied to find out what the action of those drugs should have been, or to observe a patient to see if the treatment was having the effect for which it was prescribed. It seems to Virginia that if you are going to go into detail on the social aspects, you ought to go into the same details on the biomedical aspects of the therapy.

Sometimes Virginia feels that nursing is now in a state of total intellectual confusion and somehow or other nurses have got to get out of it. As she sees it, instead of complicating and elaborating the care, nurses ought to simplify it, and isolate the essentials. She also thinks the patient ought to be given a copy of any health records.

Virginia believes that there is nothing nursing could do that would establish its value to the patient as much as to try to get some international model of a good health record; then the patient could go from one country to another and present to whatever agency a record that will show he has been treated elsewhere — so that they would not have to start from scratch. She thinks it is essential to verify what is important in a health record, to use standard language that can be understood as present records are full of jargon. 'Clean up the language. Make a copy for the patient. A nineteen-year old man writing in *Time* magazine sees the point of putting it on a chip so that you can carry it with you.' She would like to see the patient prepared to play a more effective role in his/her own care and much better health education.

One way to improve people's education, she argues, is to give them a copy of their record, so they can at least find out what professionals think is wrong with them and what tests have been done. It is so hard for Virginia to understand why everybody does not agree with her! It seems so obvious to her. The fact that it is done for US military personnel shows that it is not an impossible thing to suggest; otherwise 'it is like running a secret society with the people being unable to have their records.'

What Virginia really hopes to stress when talking about professional health workers' interdependence is that those workers who are taking care of the patient ought to have a common purpose, for if they have different purposes, it is very confusing for the patient and often harmful. To some extent, the nursing process has separated nurses and doctors, in her view; it has become a wedge between the doctor and the nurse, rather than something that encouraged interdependence in the establishment of a common purpose for the patient.

Her main concern is that too much time is being spent on the various theoretical approaches and that nurses are trying to describe models in terminology that is both vague and cannot be understood. Cautiously, Virginia says, 'I myself, when I write about this, have to quote people rather than translate it, because I am not sure that I can translate it.' Even the American Nurses' Association statement on what nursing is, is not as clear as it might be, she argues.

Nevertheless, Virginia concedes that there are ideas that have come out of these activities that have been very helpful. She thinks that Martha Rogers's emphasis on the relationship between the patient and the nurse being a changing one is good. Martha Rogers is a nursing theorist whose work emphasises 'holistic' nursing care. Her ideas are expounded in *An Introduction to the Theoretical Basis of Nursing* (published in 1970 by F A Davis, Philadelphia). Virginia thinks there is an essence in all the theories that is useful but she would like all the theoretical statements simplified and demonstrated in practice. She would also like to see the use of them being measured in terms of what happens to the patient. Virginia believes that what is sadly lacking in nursing is some measurement of the effectiveness of what nurses are doing and the effect on the receiver of that care. As she says, 'The emphasis in the literature has been on the provider of nursing rather than on the recipient. I think that it is time that we changed that emphasis. I would hate to go down in history as somebody who opposed this analysis. I just want to see the analysis made by people who understand how to apply it and, if possible, note the effects of it. I am sometimes considered a theorist and at other times not a theorist.'

Virginia's view and definition of nursing have also had their critics. Some claim that the perspective does not take a holistic approach, a criticism she totally rejects: 'I am one of the few people who sees the patient whole enough to say you ought to know something about their religion, because that is the source of their values', she points out, and continues to argue that 'I am one of the few people who have explained that if you want to nurse a patient well, you should think of all aspects of their life. I don't see how you can take care of a person without realising that they have various functions. I don't see how you can teach or write about nursing unless you separate those functions and talk about how to deal with those functions. I see people all the time who are hunched over in bed being taken care of by people who may be holistic, but they are not watching the person's posture to see that the lungs can expand normally.'

Virginia certainly has no wish to go down in history as an opponent of studying the theoretical aspects of nursing, for she believes she has demonstrated the application of theory in the sources that she used in arriving at her concept of nursing. Her challenge is that 'I wish everyone who wrote about the theory of nursing would practise enough and would be helpful enough to tell us how to convert their theory of nursing into nursing practice.'

Reading Virginia's definition of nursing convinces one that she has a point. Her own philosophy and concept of nursing are made abundantly clear. Her words are enshrined for posterity both in her textbook *Principles and Practice of Nursing* and the International Council of Nurses' publication *Basic Principles of Nursing Care*. It reads as follows:

> 'The unique function of the nurse is to assist the individual, sick or well, in the performance of those activities contributing to health or its recovery (or to a peaceful death) that he would perform unaided if he had the necessary strength, will or knowledge. And to do this in such a way as to help him gain independence as rapidly as possible. This aspect of her work, this part of her function, she initiates and controls; of this she is master. In addition she helps the patient to carry out the therapeutic plan as initiated by the physician. She also, as a member of a medical team, helps other members, as they in turn help her, to plan and carry out the total program whether it be for the improvement of health, or the recovery from illness or support in death.'

CHAPTER 10

Influences of Religion

The religious experiences that influenced Virginia more than anything else were the simple Episcopalian services that her grandfather conducted for the boys in his school. The school was fifteen or more miles from the town and the churches in that community, during the winter, were not available to the boys; so they either had to go without a church service or grandfather had to conduct it. Reading grandfather's and grandmother's letters to each other when they were engaged, and later, has made Virginia realise that grandmother was much more personally religious than grandfather, and much more conventionally religious than grandfather. He must have had a very well-developed discriminatory sense of what was appropriate for him to present in those services and he read two sets of sermons by religious authors over and over again.

Grandfather was a lay reader in the Episcopalian Church. The room that was devoted to chapel services was empty all week. It was full of benches and had a little organ, and grandmother, a distinguished musician as far as the piano and organ were concerned, played music that was appropriate for the services.

All the family loved to go to the services — and the boys, too. As far as she can remember, the people who sang best were collected on a bench in front of the organ and were responsible for leading the rest. Virginia looked forward to those services. It was not a question of 'you have to go to church': they *wanted* to do it. There was a lovely little red-bricked church to which the family went during summer — and still go to — about five miles away; and that was another event that they used to look forward to with the greatest possible pleasure. The whole local community streamed over on Sunday mornings to the service at this church, which was not opened during the winter months because the roads were so bad. In later years, after grandfather died, there was a lay reader who used to conduct services in the church. He was very much amused one day, when he was getting ready to come out in his vestments, because her sister, Jane, said, 'Well, I think my worst dream is realised. You are here reading the service and I am here to play the organ and there is nobody in the congregation!'

In later years when father no longer had his office in Washington and mother and father were at Trivium all the time, mother used her influence to get that church going the whole time. Virginia was commissioned to buy all kinds of things for the church, and her mother embroidered others. That church has been very much a part of the Hendersons' life. Virginia thinks that grandfather's services perhaps set the stage for her thinking of religion in very literal terms. At any rate, she was tremendously interested in it.

During a church convocation, in her early teens, Virginia worked hard to get the meals for everybody who came and, she says, 'I must have been very pious at that time, because a thunderstorm came, and instead of having a picnic outdoors the food was brought into the church, and it troubled me very much. I didn't think it was appropriate to eat in the church. I remember a young minister at that convocation named Frank Nelson, he was a lovely, lovely man, and he was very interested in my distress, and he sat down and talked to me all during that meal about what the church stood for, and how artificial in a way he made me feel it was to believe that you could or could not, should or should not, eat in a church. I think it influenced me about what the church should really mean to people.'

Gradually Virginia began to want to know about other religions and her mother took it seriously. When the children made Christmas lists, asking for what they would like, Virginia asked for the Koran because she wanted to know about its teachings. Mother gave her the Koran but Virginia was bitterly disappointed because she could not really enjoy it. It was not organised in a way that made it easy for her to get out of it what the Muslims get out of their Holy Book.

At night, when the little boys went to bed, she read the Bible aloud to them. She hoped it would have some civilising influence.

Looking back on her childhood, Virginia realises she must have been very much influenced by the Christian religion — but open to the influence of other religions. She was relatively free from prejudice against the other denominations in the protestant church, which she always felt was, to some extent, rooted in a snobbish concept of which denomination the right people belonged to, and the relationship between the denomination and one's position in society.

She was very interested in the services she was taken to in which the black people participated. To this day she does not like calling people 'black' but recognises that 'it is their response to our calling ourselves "white". I think it is unfortunate, we always spoke of them as "negroes".' When she went to the funerals of black people or to their services, they all sang so lustily when they responded to the minister during the service, and she found she liked it. She liked the feeling of spontaneous response.

It has been very hard for Virginia to separate religion, ethics and philosophy: for her, they blur as soon as she begins to use the concepts. Needless to say, it has always been very difficult for her to understand how people could get up in a pulpit and say, during wartime, that 'the Lord is on our side.' 'How they can be that sure on what the Lord is thinking is beyond me', she often says. 'How people who claim to be Christians and think that it is right for us to pin medals all over the chest of a man who has killed hundreds in the war? It just causes me to gasp because it is so far from the way I think.'

Virginia would like to think that people in any church should at least have some knowledge of all religions. She believes that mankind ought to be searching for a common denominator and finds comfort in the knowledge that the members of the Bahai religion are trying to establish a formal religion that would embrace all religions, with a common religious basis towards human behaviour. She looks upon religion as a source of values, thinking that if you believe one thing is right and constantly do something that is wrong according to your faith, it should make you tremendously disturbed. A friend of her Aunt Lucy's once said something that set her thinking. 'We were talking about religion and he was saying he would be a Christian if he ever met one, and I know exactly what he was talking about. We mouth the beliefs of Christ but we don't follow them. We find all kinds of excuses for deviating from what Christ taught.'

Together with her niece, Delia, when she was training as a nurse in New York, Virginia used to do the rounds of all the religious services. 'Sunday after Sunday she would come down and join me and we would go to services that were available on Sunday in New York City, and there were many of them, of course. Some of those were very memorable to me. One was the Quaker service where we sat in silence for a long time. It was very strange to us because, of course, we never had silent meditating periods in our services in the Episcopal services. We went to Presbyterian Churches and Roman Catholics', Methodists' and Baptists' as well. Then on Fridays we went to the Synagogue.'

One of the most interesting services they went to was conducted by Hindus on the first floor of a brown-stoned front house on Fifth Avenue. The Swami said something that set Virginia thinking again. He said there were as many religions as there were people in the world and she thought that was a pretty demoralising but accurate statement. She recalls: 'I thought, you are for me. It enabled me to understand the Hindu religious writings.'

Virginia became particularly interested in the Quakers and began to see that their beliefs enabled them to be sympathetic with all the peoples of the world, in wartime even with the 'enemy'. So she 'became especially interested in the Quaker religion. I read a good deal written by Quakers. If I had to name a religion that suited me better than any other, it would be expressed by the Quakers.'

Virginia has tried all her life to read things on the behaviour of people, according to their religious background. 'One of the things that I liked best was discovering that Buddah, after he was a young man, left his home and family and meditated. After meditating and meditating for several years, he re-entered the world with a conviction, which was a guiding principle for him, that from good comes good, and from evil comes evil.' So she thinks that possibly confirmed her in her conviction about pacifism.

Despite her early difficulties with the Koran, Virginia believes she got something very constructive out of the Muslim faith and that is that they consider all religious leaders, including Christ, as one of their prophets; but Mohammed was their great prophet. 'That strikes me as a constructive element in their belief', she says. 'I think it has enabled them perhaps to be as effective as they have been in certain periods of history. For instance, the development of Spain by the Muslims has very many constructive elements. So much of the beautiful architecture stems from their occupation and leadership in Spain.'

Not surprisingly, Virginia finds the present ecumenical spirit in the Christian churches encouraging and she has a conviction 'that many ministers follow my liberal views but are afraid to share them with their congregations, because the congregations are so conservative.'

Religious beliefs have undoubtedly affected Virginia's philosophy of life, just like her heroine 'Mother Theresa, who helps people without discrimination or reservations, who says "I see in every person Jesus Christ." She never rejects any human being. I suppose that means that I would like to think that as I have nursed people, that I have a certain capacity for loving everybody that I have nursed, because, I don't believe that anybody is all bad.' Her own philosophy has created a recent intensive interest in the plight of prisoners. She says a prison 'is one place that I like to go in every country so that I can get some idea if other countries are as remiss as we are. I went to jail in New York City which was a most horrible place. The windows were so dirty that very little light came through them. The equipment in the unit where they took care of people if they needed a wound dressed was furnished with chipped enamel ware that was discarded from the city hospitals. How that experience could fail to bother us people I don't see. The thing that was most shocking was to find that in jails half of the inmates had never been convicted. They have never been tried, and they are waiting trial. So that they might be perfectly innocent.'

Virginia points out, with feeling, that the Quakers thought that there would be a real *reformation* programme in the jails. 'Well, that was lost sight of long ago. The nursing profession has practically washed their hands of it.' That is her view and it annoys her that in the USA it costs $17,000 a year to keep someone in prison. 'More than going to college!'

Virginia feels very strongly about the lack of rehabilitation programmes in prison. 'Many decades ago I tried to clarify how I nursed by saying what I thought the nurse's unique function was, which was to do for others what they would do for themselves if they had the necessary skill, strength and knowledge, and to do it in such a way that they would be independent of help. I was in that way saying I believe every patient ought to be rehabilitated. I think we ought to have the principles of rehabilitation in our minds whenever we are nursing.'

In her unique definition of nursing, Virginia claims that she is 'expressing a philosophy about the relationship of human beings to each other, and I am trying to say that I don't consider nurses uniquely compassionate, uniquely willing to do things for anybody that they need to have done because they lack will, strength and knowledge. I have had doctors who have been very willing to do that. I had a surgeon who, after operating on me came down with my special nurse and said, "I would like to stay with Virginia, while you go to your lunch." I have had doctors who have, to me, been just as compassionate. A nurse also helps a person to die a peaceful death, and that suggests to me that you try to provide the person with whatever religious consolation they can find in the representatives of their faith who can share their doubts, their fears, their sorrows and give them consolation in whatever faith they have. I have given, I think, a broader function of nursing than I have seen in any other definition, or any other theory or model. I think it is the only model that mentions helping a person to die well, what is essentially, to me, a religious obligation. So I try to say how you apply this definition. I look at different things in a person's behaviour that show that they need help, and that indicate the kind of help they might need. One of the things you do is to give them an opportunity to practise their religion and to act in such a way so they don't feel that they are transgressing what religion has imposed on them all their life. So, in a positive sense, you try and supply them with the people who will support them, and you will also try and provide them with a diet that they can eat without feeling guilty. You give them time, if possible, to go outside the institution for what help they get from their religion.'

If Virginia is asked, 'If you were in the practice situation now, how would you react, for example, to having to turn off the respirator of a young man who was twenty-four?', she replies, without hesitation, 'I have no answer to all of these dilemmas.' But she is quick to add that she would never do any of these things without an opportunity for the care-givers, patient or close family, to participate in the decision. 'I would not feel comfortable carrying the responsibility for a decision that I considered as vital to human welfare and happiness by myself. I don't know the answers to these things, but I think that human beings ought to have a choice. I think the people involved ought to be given the opportunity to participate.'

Virginia is open-minded about euthanasia. She thinks that a person should be allowed to practise euthanasia and argues that forcing people to live, who are saying daily, 'I want to die', is all wrong. She regrets that 'we extend a life that no longer has meaning, purpose or enjoyment' and thinks that is wrong. In her view, life has no useful purpose when the person says his life has no useful purpose, and when the family agrees that it will be a relief to them when he is dead. 'They don't want to see suffering.'

Virginia is quite clear that she would not treat an AIDS patient any differently from the way she would treat anybody else. She would certainly try and protect other people from being infected by the AIDS patient. 'I don't think I am going to impose on anybody else any concepts I have about the rightness or wrongness of human behaviour. In any case, the AIDS question has long since been divorced from being solely a homosexual dilemma. Too many people of both sexes have it now.' She believes, like many other people, that it is going to grow and become such an over-whelming problem and could well dominate every other health program-me. 'We speak of communicable disease as having dominated the first decades of this century, because our chief causes of death were pneumonia, influenza and respiratory infections. We think we have controlled that, and now AIDS comes along and throws us right back into this dilemma of having to learn enough about a condition to eliminate the cause, and improve the inadequate treatment of it that often occurs.'

She certainly does not share the concern of some people who are expressing concern about the vast amount of resources that are being re-directed from other health care programmes to the AIDS programme. She does think not enough resources are being directed towards it, adding that 'I think the cause has been confused with the question of sexual behaviour. It has been taboo to talk about it, and to work with it.'

If Virginia is asked about her views on life after death, a typical response is: 'I think we waste our lives worrying about what is going to happen after we die. We can't possibly control it, and it is much better to think about and give our attention to things that we can do something about. I suppose some people call me an agnostic. I don't consider myself an agnostic. I believe in an after-life because I think that the life you have lived influences the people around you. So I consider everybody has an after-life in the memory of the people who have known them, and in the effect of anything that they have done. That is one reason why I think it is terribly important to try and think that — as the Buddists say — from good comes good, and from evil comes evil. I think the evil you do lives after you, and the good you do lives after you, and I think you ought to concern youself with what is what in this life much more than what is going to happen to you when you die. How people can believe in cremation, and then believe you will rise again in the clothes you were wearing, is beyond me, but if anybody believes it, I am willing to admit that they may be just as right as I am. It does not disturb me.'

Virginia cannot help but see love as part of the spiritual dimension of men and woman and argues that nurses do love their patients. 'An inability to love a patient is felt by them and is destructive to them', she says. Focusing on love in nursing leads her naturally to a comment on hospice care. 'I think probably the best thing that has happened to health care in this age is what has happened to the terminally ill through the hospice movement.' That movement, she is convinced, has a great deal to teach those involved in general health care programmes, but in Virginia's view 'much of our hospital environment is conducive to making you sick rather than well.' Whereas in a hospice, she points out, 'pain is controlled, and the discomfort of the illness is controlled to the optimum extent, so the pain does not interfere with leading a relatively normal life.'

In the final alalysis, Virginia argues that spirituality and 'religiosity' are different things and thinks you can be a very spiritual person and have no religious beliefs. It will be quite effective, she argues, 'if you express a constructive philosophy and if you have a code of ethics that is as protective to other people's welfare as your own, and if you are willing to do everything that you can conceive as being useful to that other person and give unselfish service.' But she adds that 'if you are religious it is probably easier for you or more common amongst religious people.' Nevertheless, cautiously, she tends to think that 'if you have a religion that is exclusive, it makes you think that people who don't hold your beliefs are inferior. It is likely to do you more harm than good if it restricts you to caring only for the people of your own faith.'

Virginia readily admits that, by and large, where hospitals are operated under religious auspices, they are giving superior care, so that she feels obliged to think that having and applying a religious belief is likely to improve rather than harm the care of people. Not surprisingly, Virginia Henderson is a great champion of the cause of ministers of religion and hospital chaplains as important members of the health care team.

In the sixth edition of her classic textbook *Principles and Practice of Nursing* (written with Gladys Nite and published by Macmillan, New York), Virginia devoted the whole of Chapter 18 to 'Worship'. In the summary of that chapter, she says: 'The knowledge health workers have of religions and their ability to serve people of any faith with understanding determines the range and quality of their usefulness.'

CHAPTER 11

The Henderson View of Politics and Nursing

Virginia Henderson grew up in an apolitical environment. When Uncle Charlie ran for some minor political office, it was a great joke, and everybody rejoiced when he did not win. A one-legged man beat him: it was a big joke.

Whenever her father was at home when they were living at Bellevue, he and her grandfather talked politics much of the time when they were together. Grandfather was not an apolitical person, but never thought of active participation in politics. He was, however, very aware of the importance of electing the right person to office. He was a person who spoke with great ease from any platform. Virginia's father was very interested in what was happening in the country politically because his work was so influenced by the political attitude towards the Indians. His cases were all fought against the American Government and he had to live in Washington DC, because that was where his battles were fought.

Virginia thinks that if she had been more aware of her father's activities she would have realised that he was a better citizen than most members of the family. The rest of the family were largely people interested in the workings of the mind, and in good conversation. People used to say about her mother's family that the worst thing you could do to an Abbot was to bore them. There was a great emphasis put on being agreeable and being entertaining, being charming and having a sense of humour.

The emphasis put on communication in the family was strong but the more serious side of being a good citizen was not really stressed. Virginia, therefore, had to develop for herself the political philosophy that duty to the world in which you live was even greater than that to the occupation or profession to which you belonged. She thinks that if she had her life to live over again she would try harder to be a good citizen and get rid of the idea that politics are not good. 'I grew up with the idea that politicians were not the nicest people in the world and that politics was an ugly word. If you said in my family that somebody was a statesman, that was a compliment, but if you said they were a politician, it was anything but. It was almost assumed that you couldn't be political and moral at the same time. You were not likely to be a politician and an intellectual at the same time. It was confused with self-seeking rather than being public-spirited.'

Virginia's association with Miss Goodrich influenced her as did her close association with her older sister (Lucy). Lucy was a very courageous person, in Virginia's view, who assumed a positive attitude towards women's suffrage because she really was one woman against the family, and people made it as hard for her as possible. She showed great courage in defending the position of the early suffragettes. Lucy had great fun made of her because she was actively engaged in supporting equal rights for women as far as the vote was concerned. Virginia points out that 'I have never been an active feminist. I think I find it distasteful to have to fight for something. I think I distinguish the need for fighting for something and standing for something. I think now I would have stood beside Lucy in the position she took.' Miss Goodrich was one of the women in New York who rode a horse up and down Fifth Avenue in the suffrage parades.

From the time Virginia qualified as a nurse she has been a member of nursing organisations and an active member from the time she started working in Virginia. Nursing organisations had to be involved in politics, Virginia believes, if they were going to accomplish anything, so she ceased to excuse herself from political activity. During the 1960s when the US students were all so actively opposing the Vietnamese war, she even flew down to Washington with a group of students and participated in their lobbying efforts. Certainly, she was known for being politically active in New Haven during the Vietnamese war, which she openly opposed there, and students and the opposing groups identified themselves with her.

Virginia remembers in the 1930s, as a very young nurse, feeling that American nurses were making a mistake in taking the decision to support the American Medical Association in its political views about health care. She recalls with deep regret her memories of the late '30s when the American Nurses' Association removed support from those nurses promoting tax-supported comprehensive health care for the USA, because the American Medical Association was opposing it. She remembers walking the length of the huge conference auditorium, with trembling knees, and saying that she thought they were making a mistake in aligning themselves with the largest faction of the American Medical Association. She did not see why they could not support the minority in the American Medical Association that was more in favour of universal, comprehensive, tax-supported health care in the USA. She got a round of applause but did not accomplish anything. Virginia regrets that, as far as she knows, the American nursing profession has never supported a section of the medical world that was for a *liberal* programme. During the 1960s about six Bills were being advocated in the US Congress and Senator Edward Kennedy was supporting one. 'They were all discussed at meetings at Yale. I remember I was always at those meetings and I was very much concerned at that time with getting tax-supported health care in this country. I wanted to hear what people said and what they were thinking. It was very troubling to me. I remember waiting to hear people speak in opposition to the Bills that I considered inadequate and discriminatory. Certainly the private insurance plans were not congenial to me. The Edward Kennedy Bill was the one that I would have been most likely to support.'

Virginia's questions at the end of these discussions were always why they thought a free National Health Service would not work for the USA, when it was working in Britain — only to be told that the USA was so large and that it was not like Britain, and that you could do it in a small place but you could not do it in a place as big as USA. Then she would say that it was being done in Russia. Recalling that, she says, 'Well, that was destructive, because that is the last thing that anyone wants — a system like Russia!'

Virginia thinks that the American health care system is chaotic and she believes in tax-supported health care in exactly the same way that everybody in America believes in tax-supported education, and she sees absolutely no difference in the principle. It is paradoxical to Virginia that the opposition to tax-funded health care persists in the USA yet all the government employees have it and all the military have it. 'The military has really wonderful health care,' she points out, 'and they enjoy the benefit which I would like for all of our citizens of owning their health records.' Furthermore, getting on to her hobby horse, she argues, 'Everybody who is in the military is given a copy of their record which they carry from one place to another. Why in the world do people oppose that for the average citizen? I think we should acknowledge that a person's health record is their property and the most important thing that you can put in their hands from the standpoint of health education. We talk about the health education of the public but we withhold the records from them. We pass State laws that say the patient's record is his property. In practice if you try and get your hands on your record, you face a blank wall.'

Virginia, however, notes a hopeful growing political consciousness among nurses starting in the 1950s. There was an exposé of the conditions in the US mental hospitals, which made everyone ashamed. This resulted in nearly every State appointing a Commission on Mental Health. Suddenly nurses in psychiatry were in great demand and you could get research funds for psychiatric studies when you could not get funds for studies in any other field. The psychiatrists were much more willing to work with the nurses as partners than the physicians, she says.

The commissions set up for mental health, on which nurses are represented, have made American nurses more politically aware, and have drawn a great many into political activity in which they had not been involved before, Virginia holds. The American Nurses' Association has set up an office in Washington DC to make it easier to lobby for Bills in which nurses are concerned. That was set up in the 1950s and now certain members of Congress promote nursing interests. Since then a Nursing Institute in Washington has been created, comparable to the other Institutes of Health. Virginia, personally, was not for it, because she thinks nursing ought to be a

Above: Virginia Henderson
as a student nurse, 1918

Below: Teacher's College, 1941 – Virginia Henderson (third from left) with some of
her classmates

Dennis Bradbury Photo

Virginia Henderson in 1988, surrounded by some of her publications

part of those ten or more institutes of health, believing that nurses have got to get nursing research supported, just like other health groups. If the physicians had been more interested in working with nurses as partners, Virginia argues, there would not have been this effort to get a research institute set up. She firmly believes that such institutes should be focused on the service given by the health worker rather than on the promotion of the interests of a particular profession. Nonetheless, Virginia concedes that the establishment of that Nursing Institute was the direct result of effective political leadership on the part of the nurses who wanted it.

As a result of the medical opposition and the private insurance opposition to get a tax-supported health care in the USA, some other means of supporting health care has had to be devised, and industry has seen this as an opportunity to make money, Virginia argues. 'So we now have what is publicly called by almost everybody the health care industry.' When an officer of the American Nurses' Association, from a platform at Yale University in 1986, referred to the health care industry, Virginia was forced to get up and say, 'Are we going to succumb to this influence in this country of industrialising health care? Are we going to give up on the idea that health care is the right of every human being and that it is a service? If health care is an industry, is there any such thing as a human service? Because if health care and education isn't a service, I don't know what is.'

In Virginia's view, doctors do not seem to be resisting this 'industralisation' because really they brought it about and are very largely responsible for it. In her view, the effect this is now having, however, is that doctors are beginning to find that they are not welcome in a hospital unless they bring a certain number of patients in. They cannot stay on the staff unless they are an industrial asset, and bringing in sufficient income. Even when a group of doctors sets up a group practice, they are not welcome to stay in that practice unless they can pull their weight financially.

Virginia is passionate about health care: 'I see health care now as politically-based and unless you get a sound political base I can't blame the health workers who I think are corrupted by the system that we have in this country, which is one that is dominated by profit motive.' But, with regret, she thinks that the nurses in the USA are not really too bothered about it.

Virginia also has particularly vitriolic words to say about feminism which is associated in her mind with the strident and antagonising personalities of some of the people who are the leaders. She likes to feel that things can be accomplished without fighting people. Maybe, she says, she holds those views because she is a pacifist and against violence. She is often accused of being an idealist as opposed to a realist. The people she admires most are those who accomplish their ends through gentler means. Ghandi is one of her heroes and Mother Theresa a heroine. Virginia tends to believe that if women stood up for their rights as individuals in their families and homes, and did not allow themselves to be brow-beaten by their husbands and brothers, they would not need to become aggressive feminists. To this day, it troubles Virginia to visit a family and see a dominant woman putting a man in an embarrassing position by wanting to be the controlling force. She just does not like it. As she puts it: 'It is hard for me to explain my position on feminism because I believe in the equality of men and women, but I also like the difference between men and women.' However, she does admire the people who were active in the suffragette movement and in all the movements that gave women equal opportunities with men. She finds it ironic that usually the women leaders of the feminist movement are not child-producing women. 'It may be because they are hard and have to impress everybody with their importance by requiring obedience from other people.' The suffragette movement was the most concrete expression of feminism that she can think of.

Switching her focus from women to men and asking her if they have made any contribution to the politicisation of nursing in the US, her reply tends to be: 'There are so few men in nursing in the US that I think that they feel to some extent powerless, and they may be oppressed by being in a profession where they are perhaps discriminated against.' In fact, Virginia does not think that in the USA many families would want their sons to be nurses. Almost any woman in the USA wants her son to be a doctor, Virginia points out, and you never hear anyone aspiring to having a son as a nurse. Virginia thinks it is quite sad and has deliberately 'always referred to "men nurses" rather than "male nurses", because somehow "female and male nurses" is not a complimentary term.'

With obvious pleasure, Virginia cites the one man in American nursing — Luther Christman — 'who seems to me to have overcome all handicaps' and ran for the office of the ANA President, but was defeated. Luther, she points out, is a member of the Honorary Society of Medicine, which, for a nurse, is almost unheard of.

Virginia has been greatly influenced by Ghandi who was one of the greatest human beings that ever lived, in her view, not least because he died for his principles. 'In fact so many people have died for their principles that you almost feel that if you live to be ninety, your principles must have been shady in some respects!' Virginia has reached her ninetieth birthday!

Early in life Virginia began to identify with great pacifists like Schweitzer and Ghandi and from childhood she considered Christ a pacifist. Tolstoy was also a great influence on her, even though she recognises that many of his writings talked about how people had discarded the teaching of Christ, because it did not fit in with their lives.

Virginia is absolutely against nuclear weapons, not only because she is a pacifist, but because we have not learnt how to destroy the waste from nuclear activity and are poisoning our environment. She cannot see nuclear power as having advanced the welfare of the human race. She is against it because if there is a war and nuclear weapons are used we will literally destroy the earth by contaminating the environment.

Virginia does not want to commit herself for posterity on what she thinks of the Reagan and Gorbachev peace initiatives but has concluded from what she reads about Gorbachev that he sounds very sincere. He and she think much more alike than Mr Reagan and Virginia, so she hopes the US Presidents in future will seek more exposure to Mr Gorbachev's ideas to remove the confidence in the use of force (that she does not share) as a means of settling differences.

Her views about Reagan do not disguise the fact that she is a member of the Democratic Party, which has shown much more of a disposition to help the underprivileged and under-endowed, in her view, and to limit the profits that can be made in industry. Certainly all the proposals for National Health Insurance come from them, she points out. 'I suppose I may have influenced other people to vote for Democratic candidates with my verbal support. But then, many people never talk about who they are going to vote for. I feel that is a pity. I don't hesitate to say who I am going to vote for. I like to talk about politics, even though I was brought up to think it was very ill-bred and bad form to talk about religion or politics.'

Another political dimension of Virginia's life and work has been her interest and support for consumer groups, self-advocate groups and patient advocate groups, pointing out that 'If you look at the writing that I have done in a very large textbook you will find that the text is saturated with that concept.'

In the 1960s Virginia tried to get the National League for Nursing to change its name to the National League for Health because in that League there is open membership that enables anybody interested in nursing to be a member. They have many non-health workers in the League, so she thinks 'I have stood four-square for the dominant role that citizenship plays, and the respect that we should show for their concept of what they need, and what is wrong.'

The nursing profession in the USA has welcomed the consumer movement more than doctors, but not nearly enough, she says. The public health nurses see this need very clearly but they are in the minority as so many nurses have not thought about it. So many of them think of themselves as responsible for giving care, rather than as helping a person to care for themselves. As prevention is very much less dramatic than cure, nurses are more likely to earn the praise and gratitude if they cure them, she admits. 'I don't suppose anybody in this country has demonstrated the effectiveness of prevention to the extent that people in AA [Alcoholics Anonymous] have. Those groups have tried to help people with a drinking problem, and are so dramatically effective.'

Virginia feels that in spite of high level nursing education in the USA, American nurses still do not have a highly developed state of political consciousness. 'I think that having elected Ronald Reagan to the Presidency twice in recent years shows that the mood of the country is conservative,' she points out. 'How do you account from a swing from a more liberal attitude during the '60s when we were very critical of the Government? How do you account for us getting into an even more conservative period than we had earlier?' Nurses, she believes, merely reflect the political conservatism of the USA. She pines for more astutely political nurses, like Miss Goodrich, who, writing in the 1930s, saw no hope for the poor without National Health Insurance: 'She had a concept that very few nurses, even in this age, hold.'

Virginia is hopeful, nevertheless, about the new generation of American nursing students. With obvious pleasure, she recalls: 'If you express a liberal view to the Yale students, as I inevitably do when they ask me to come over and talk to them, I get a very sympathetic response. They are always pleased to hear it. These are mature people. They are not as young as most nursing students and many of them have had experience in the Peace Corps or in some other group, particularly for the underprivileged.'

Virginia thinks that British nurses are much more politically astute than American nurses, not least because she understands that, 'in educated circles, political questions are more likely to be the topic of conversation at a dinner party than they are in the USA!' She feels sure that the International Council of Nurses has done something to politicise nursing but finds it very hard to identify what it has done.

One of ICN's former Presidents, Margarethe Kruse (1969–73), from Denmark, was a person who had done something very noteworthy in the political arena, she points out, in a major International Labour Organisation study, which included nursing problems; but she was frustrated by conservative attitudes, too, Virginia believes. For example, 'I think she wanted to get Russian nurses into the ICN. I think they were not thought eligible because the nursing organisations in Russia, I believe, were not thought to be under the control of the nursing occupation.' (Miss Kruse held the ICN post while being General Secretary of the Danish Nurses' Association.)

While doing that study for ILO, Miss Kruse inevitably became involved in the literature on labour and Virginia thinks she realised, as she did, that one of nursing's great weaknesses was failure to use the literature. 'It seems to me so short-sighted that the ICN did not realise that,' Virginia often says, recalling her own work in organising a major exhibition at the ICN Quadrennial Congress in Montreal, Canada, in 1969. That exhibition has never been repeated. 'I think that tells us a lot,' Virginia says, 'I think we have not grown up yet as a profession. If you can't find out what nurses are writing or what people are writing about nursing, you have no way of being a really professional worker.'

Virginia recalls that one of the last major political decisions that ICN made was during 1973 at the meeting in Mexico when they expelled South

Africa. 'I wonder, if you had a view, whether you felt that was a politically astute decision, or a politically naive one? They expelled South Africa because black nurses were unable to hold executive positions. I would have been unsympathetic with that move. I would have said that was definitely political. I would have kept them in if I could by some means.' Virginia is, of course, strongly opposed to apartheid. She suspects that that was one of the decisions that was not personally supported by Miss Kruse (who was ICN President at the time), but no matter what her views were, she had to go along with the decision. 'I know that she left that post a saddened person because she could not persuade the ICN Board to see things as she saw them', Virginia believes, and adds that 'I formed the opinion that she was a very outstanding thinker, and ahead of her time.' Virginia does not believe that anybody has emerged since with Miss Kruse's kind of political stature in the nursing profession.

CHAPTER 12

After Retirement —
International Nurse

Virginia Henderson was seventy-five years old when she completed the *Nursing Index* work in 1972. She was then created Senior Research Associate Emeritus at Yale University School of Nursing and later Yale University awarded her an honorary doctorate. But she certainly did not retire. Far from it. She then started what to most people under fifty would be a killing schedule of national and international speeches, consultations and attendances at professional meetings, seminars and conferences. Even in her ninety-first year she flew from a meeting on the East coast of the USA to a conference on the West coast (the same distance as New York to London, England) and then on to a conference in Belfast, Northern Ireland, all within a period of a couple of weeks!

Honorary membership of many nurses associations and numerous honorary doctorates have been conferred on her. She has been elected a Fellow of the American Academy of Nursing (FAAN) and, in 1978, she was created a Fellow of the Royal College of Nursing of the United Kingdom. On her ninetieth birthday, the Royal College of Nursing created her one of its Vice Presidents for life.

At the International Council of Nursing's Quadrennial Congress in 1985, held in Tel Aviv, Israel, Virginia Henderson was awarded the first ICN Christianne Reimann Award for her distinguished contribution to nursing throughout the world.

During her many journeys she has travelled extensively to many of the States in the USA. In addition, she has accepted invitations to visit nurses and nursing organisations in Australia, Canada, Denmark, England, France, Northern Ireland, the Republic of Ireland, Israel, Japan, Norway, Pakistan, Scotland, Spain, Switzerland and Wales. Her diary is usually committed well in advance and she is in such demand that sometimes she has, with regret, to decline some of the invitations.

She also still gets a great deal of fun at classes and seminars with nursing students everywhere but especially at the Yale University School of Nursing where she takes her role as an honorary faculty member very seriously indeed.

Canada

Her experiences in Canada have been coloured by the fact that she had many remarkably fine women students from that country who studied at Teacher's College. Some of the happiest memories that she has are of working with those students. So that when she goes to Canada: 'I feel as if I am in a way back home. I am very fond of Canadians anyway. They are the best-mannered people that I have ever worked with. I have never met a Canadian who was pretentious or affected. Their manners seem to me to be like the well-mannered adults that I knew as a child. They seem to have escaped a good many of the pitfalls that people in this country have fallen into!'

When Virginia says that she feels that she is going back to the atmosphere of her youth, she hastens to add, 'I am paying them a compliment.' The first time she went there was for a two weeks' workshop. People who worked together in the same environment decided to change the way in which they would work in the future, which was very satisfying to her.

The University of Ontario has awarded Virginia an honorary degree. The students there presented her with the cap and gown. It is the only one she owns, so she often turns up at American events in this gown and hood from the University of Ontario.

Virginia argues that the Canadian nurses have accomplished something that US nurses have not. They have an outstanding nursing library at the nursing headquarters, which is available to anybody. Virginia believes the library in Canada is really outstanding. Equally outstanding so far as Virginia is concerned is the Canadian National Health Insurance in which care is available to all. It is not the same as the British system but it is comparable. It was set up with a great deal of opposition from certain elements of the medical profession but she points out that the nursing influence helped to get it established. 'The nurses in Canada have a much more independent voice than we have', she believes. Virginia also believes that the famous Miss Goodrich would say today, as she said in the 1930s, 'I see no help for the poor without National Health Insurance'. She does not think US Medicare programmes have been adequate in the attempt to meet the needs of the underprivileged.

She has always been impressed with the collaborative relationship between doctors and nurses in Canada which is very good, she says.

As an honorary member of one of their provincial organisations she gets their newsletter and she is very impressed with the political influence that nurses are exerting in Canada. As an example, there was a time a few years ago when doctors were trying to get legislation that would make it possible for them to charge fees in excess of that allowed by the system. She believes that the nurses, who thought that was wrong, were partially responsible for preventing that from happening.

It is interesting if you study the nursing in Canada, Virginia points out, that there seems to be more progress in one province than another. It is possible that in some provinces nurses are more politically astute. Undoubtedly, in her view, the former Executive Director of the Canadian Nurses' Association (CNA), Ginette Rogers (until 1989), 'who is a well-educated and talented woman', has been a great asset. She is very aware of the necessity of the nurses realising their full potential, Virginia believes.

When asked about nursing research in Canada, Virginia replies, 'I think the kind of research that they do will be more likely to be focused on constructive change. I feel that Canadian nurses are very much involved in the practice of nursing. I think that American nurses have spent too much time studying nurses and not their function. They have been concerned with studies of their educational preparation. Perhaps that is the reason why we have so much progress in the education of nurses. Whether it is progress in the right direction I think is open to question. If our progress had been directed better we would see more change in practice due to this research.'

Denmark

Denmark is another country that Virginia has had contact with and she loves to talk about Denmark because, being a staunch pacifist, the very fact that their shield has on it — 'love and strength' — appeals to her. To her it seems the most peace-loving country in the world and one of the happiest countries. Everybody meets you with a smile and is ready to laugh. 'I know there must be some poverty but there is never any sign of it', she says, and then enthusiastically adds, 'it is the most democratic place that I go to. They have no servile instincts. I always felt as if a college professor was driving me in a taxi cab. I had no sense of class distinction in Denmark. They all have good manners and look well-dressed and fed. I have never had anything but good food in Denmark. Their diet and cooking seem to me to be extremely good. I like their architecture and furnishings.'

Nursing education in Denmark must be good, she believes, to produce the kind of nurses that she met there, but admits that comparison with nursing schools in the USA is difficult because their university system is different, as is their whole system of educating and training nurses.

She recalls an extraordinary hospital in Copenhagen. It is a low building with a high tower, which is exactly the way the UN headquarters is built in New York. 'This low building where you enter is so full of art work that I am told people go there just to see it. You ascend on escalators to the second floor and there you find facilities for any sort of convention that you can think of — with an amphitheatre the like of which I have never seen anywhere. It is all rosy red. I was taken around the hospital and I have never seen anything to compare with the use of colour as in that hospital. I think that they had discovered that the warm colours have an effect on people that is very desirable. I was very impressed by all the people I met in the hospital and the whole atmosphere of the place.'

Evidence of the democratic atmosphere of Denmark was demonstrated in the behaviour of the nurses Virginia met there. The Dean of one establishment gave a great deal of her time to Virginia, but it was evident that she had distributed amongst her faculty the responsibility of 'hostessing' Virginia, so you had the feeling that every bit of responsibility did not reside in the hands of the head person. There was a sharing of responsibility, which Virginia commends. 'We went to dinner the first night at the Danish Nurses' Association', Virginia recalls. 'It is a large one-storey building. The dining room was a huge room with paintings on the wall. The dinner was delightful and after the meal we went to another room with an open fireplace and on every little table there was a basket filled with wonderful sweetmeats. They were not only delicious but so pretty to look at.'

Republic of Ireland

Some years ago, in 1982, Virginia was invited to a conference, made up of representatives of English-speaking countries, held in the Republic of Ireland. She was impressed that the nursing leadership was making a definite effort to find out where they were and where they might go.

At the time of her visit the schools of nursing were all under hospital control and it seemed to her that the matrons were a special breed. Some of them still wore Irish lace collars on their uniforms. One of the matrons had a lovely apartment in the hospital, she recalls. 'She had all the facilities for entertaining. It was really like something from the past century.' In one hospital she visited there was a most magnificent library. It was an absolute treasure for books with first editions of famous books. The room was kept locked because it was known to be full of priceless treasures. Virginia 'thought it was a very exciting room. There was an air of grandeur in this hospital.'

In the Republic of Ireland she attended a conference focused on research but she did not get much of an impression that the research being done was clinically focused, or that it was having much effect on practice. When she said this at one of the seminar meetings she felt guilty about it because she thought it sounded like a criticism, but it was because she thinks nurses 'have lost a lot of time by continuing to study the problems with which we can get most help from the social scientists.' She does, however, plead that 'the excuse for me is that I have spent so many years at Teacher's College working with groups of nurses on very practical problems.' She discovered that as they talked about nursing research in Ireland, it was pretty obvious that Irish nurses had invited people from other countries to come in and talk about it. They had not, at that time, been in a position to practise it.

In Ireland Virginia had the feeling that the nursing administrators really had their finger on the pulse of the clinical care. They also ran that conference. 'The Matron who took me to her wonderful hospital was as much at home in every inch of that hospital that we visited as I would be in my own apartment,' Virginia says, and adds 'in a way it was a delightful experience for me because we know that in this country if we want a good bedside nurse, you cannot do any better than to get an Irish nurse. I had noticed that in the New York Hospital where I had experience, if we had a VIP come in and they needed a special nurse, they were quite often assigned someone from Ireland. I saw exactly why. The nursing care was second nature to them.'

Irish nursing students spent a lot of time in clinical practice. Interestingly enough, the students in Ireland, at that time, were paid almost as much as the staff nurses, which, in a way, was fair, in Virginia's view, because they were giving the care, in the same way that American students were giving the nursing care until the 1930s.

The conference took place in the Guild House of the College of Surgeons, 'a dramatically beautiful building.' They had a marvellous banquet and the President of the Republic of Ireland was there and Virginia had the privilege of sitting beside him. 'I had the impression that he was going to give his backing to the nurses, and to bring nursing more in line with modern thinking', Virginia believes. She has never seen so many people laughing and having a good time as then. In spite of the reported poverty in Ireland, she got the impression of a happy people, and the entertainment that they provided for their nurses was exceptional. 'It was a delightful experience' is the way Virginia summed it up.

Australia

Virginia was also invited to go to Australia to participate in quite a long teaching conference and workshop. Knowing nothing about Australia she read some novels about it beforehand. Never one for missing a pleasure, she stopped off in Hawaii on her way to Sydney.

At the time the schools of nursing were owned and dominated by hospitals. The students were paid very generously so it was doubtful, in her view, whether the students were supporting the efforts of the graduate nurses who were trying to get their schools out of hospitals. The few college-based programmes that existed did not seem to her to be very well attended. Virginia attributed that to the fact that nursing students were earning a good deal as they were studying in the hospital schools of nursing.

This conference was very well attended; nurses also attended from New Zealand and England. Although she was there for at least two weeks she never went out of Sydney because they worked so hard. Entertainment in the evening was with other members of the workshop, so they tended to be continually engrossed in discussion on nursing, but for Virginia 'It was an unforgettable experience. All the entertainment provided was a lot of fun. I found the people I was working with there great fun. I think we accomplished a great deal in that workshop.'

She recalls that during that workshop she had luncheon meetings with people in the administration of the State of New South Wales. That State seemed to have recently acquired some young politicians who were very ready to discuss with the visitors the possibility of radical changes in nursing education. Virginia thinks that she was probably in on the beginning of the radical change that eventually was accomplished. They are now moving their nursing education into colleges of higher education.

The impression with which Virginia left Australia was that nurses and doctors were working very closely together. The nurses had not yet effected anything like a partnership but there was a good deal of interest by the medical profession in the nurses that perhaps, she felt, it was not going to be difficult for them to effect a change. She had a feeling from the physicians she met that 'there was a willingness to help each other, and meet each other half-way.'

Her impression about nursing research activities there was that there was very little of it, but 'there is quite a lot about nursing research now', she gently points out. From about 1985 work started on a national directory of nursing research and Virginia is fascinated by the interesting nursing research activity that now goes on in Australia.

She also met a number of men nurses in Australia who seemed to be taking a pretty prominent role in nursing administration and practice there. 'I was impressed with them', she says. 'I went to the house of one of them and met his family and enjoyed it very much. Another one that I can remember took a very active role in the discussion. I seem to remember that he was involved in something that you might call research.' She also 'had a feeling of vitality in that country. An eagerness to improve their practice.'

In Australia, Virginia had the impression of a very vital society that was making very rapid changes and had accomplished much. She also 'had the feeling that nursing by men in that country was well-received and encouraged. The men nurses that I met had considerable personality. One was a psychiatric specialist, and he had ideas. I had great hospitality there.'

She was impressed with the fact that almost the entire population was covered by National Health Insurance, far ahead of anything that the US has done, she is quick to add. In view of their progressive health care system it was so hard for her to understand why their nursing education was not any more advanced than it was, but she is very happy that they have redressed that difference now.

Japan

Virginia's visit to Japan in 1982 was different from any experience that she had had so far. The extravagant planning that seemed to have gone into her visit and the number of professionals who came to the two lectures that she gave, and the 'royal' treatment that she received, almost made her feel that she should 'behave as a person from another planet'. She was totally unprepared and overawed by her treatment. She was sent a first class ticket, 'which was different from anything that I had experienced at that time', she says, and flew over the North Pole, which made her trip very short. Six people came to meet her in two black American limousines with white linen covers on the backs of the seats. She had never seen that before. If she expressed any interest in anything, they would endeavour to take her there.

Another aspect of Japanese hospitality that impressed Virginia was that she was asked by her hosts whether she had any physical disabilities they did not know about. She thought 'Why have I not said that to people, because we so often ask people to do things that are bad for them, such as walking up steps or eating things that they shouldn't?' She explained that she was once poisoned by onions, 'and for the two weeks that I was in Japan I was never served anything with onions.' That, she admits, was quite an accomplishment for the Japanese cooks.

She was taken to a beautiful hotel, which was opposite the grounds of the Emperor's palace, and was given a suite — with sitting room, bedroom and bath. There were fresh flowers and fruit the whole time she was there.

She was totally unprepared for the elegance of the luncheon party that she was taken to the day after she arrived. She still remembers with great affection the kindness and charm of her Japanese hosts and interpreters. Certainly, the hospitality throughout her stay was outstanding.

The Japanese nurses' organisation seemed so superior, she recalls. Nurses were beautifully housed. The library that they have at nursing headquarters in Tokyo is available to any nursing student, or any citizen studying nursing. It is comparable to the Royal College of Nursing's Library of Nursing.

She was told that a businessman had been to the Temple every day for two weeks before she came to pray for the success of her visit and the organising committee had so thoroughly advertised her first lecture that the very large theatre was filled. 'They had an endurance for listening that I have never encountered anywhere', Virginia says. 'They interpreted my lectures sentence by sentence.'

Both in Tokyo and Kyoto they had an intermission during which the audience was asked to write questions, which she answered in the second half. That is what she likes best. 'It is a more vital way of reaching an audience', in her view. She was also 'so impressed with the use that they made of flowers. In both cases there was a border of flowers around the stage, which added a lot to the atmosphere.'

The visit to Tokyo was very much enhanced for Virginia by being taken to a hospital. She was treated like royalty on the visit because the hospital director, the Chief Medical Officer, and the Chief of the Nursing Service and departmental heads were involved in the hospitality for her, and in setting up groups of nurses from different parts of the hospital who discussed the current problems with her in the same question and answer form that she likes. She 'felt as if the doctors took the leadership at these meetings but there was relatively little resistance on the part of the nurses.' She thinks that is understandable when, traditionally, after a woman in Japan marries, she seldom continues her professional work.

Virginia remembers that the nurses in the hospital asked if American nurses worked after they were married. In reply, she recalls, 'I told them about some hospitals that I happened to know about that 70 per cent of nurses were married women. They were amazed and said that their men would not let them do that. I remember the doctor who was leading this discussion told them that they should work on their men to make them let them work after they were married. He implied that [the hospital] needed them'. She did, however, meet some women who were in high positions in the nursing organisation who were married.

Virginia does not think that she has ever been to any country that seems to be as spotlessly clean as Japan. Their environment was so free from odours, she says.

They have a National Health Insurance system that provides care for everybody. Their occupational health care in the industries is way ahead of most because they not only provide a medical service, but they provide recreational facilities, emphasising preventive medicine. They encourage physical exercise during the working day. One of the things that impressed Virginia most was that if you were not employed, and aged seventy and over, district nurses and doctors have to go to visit you in your home, if you need care.

The Government mails you a medical record and they have to enter anybody who serves you on the record. Not surprisingly, Virginia constantly says, 'I would love to see a copy of this because it is one of the things that I talk about. I see it as a most important document in a programme of prevention and patient education to show them what diagnosis they have been given, and treatment prescribed. To me, it is a height of folly that we have not done this, and I don't understand why we are afraid to commit ourselves.'

Virginia was also impressed with Japanese community nursing services. She thinks they have very good community nursing and a very good health service. Gradually nursing education was beginning to move into colleges and universities. A number of Virginia's publications have also been translated into Japanese.

Virginia is quick to point out that if you read the history of nursing in Japan you will be amazed at the extent to which American nurses, as missionaries, dominated the education of the nurses up until fairly recent times. The nurses' headquarters contains the framed photographs of many American nurses who have contributed to their system. Therefore, Virginia's writings are not foreign to them because of the influence of other American nurses. The writings of the people who spent most of their working life there are very worth reading, in Virginia's view. Japanese nurses are very grateful to those early American nurses who devoted their lives to teaching the Japanese nurses. They have also been very influenced by the writings and teachings of Florence Nightingale.

Virginia left Japan with much respect for the personal discipline which exists there. 'Both imposed from above and self-imposed, they have ability to accomplish wonders, because they are so disciplined. I saw nothing but orderly behaviour. My impression is of a disciplined, orderly, industrious country, which seems to have the ability to discover what is good in other cultures, and adapt it to their own, and make the best possible use of it.' Virginia was also impressed with the workers and their work and the way the patients looked, and the way they were treated, and also by the co-operative relationship between doctors and nurses she observed in the hospital.

Norway

Virginia was invited to Norway in 1987 to participate in a meeting to celebrate the seventy-fifth anniversary of the Nurses' Association. There were speakers from many countries. She considers it to be one of the more advanced countries in nursing, although they have not yet got their doctoral programmes under way. She feels that the public image of nursing in Norway is good. They have accepted and tried to implement the recommendations of the World Health Organisation and have a good tax-supported health care system; and the nurses' role in it is recognised as a very important one, Virginia believes.

She was put up in a famous hotel and her suite faced a busy corner, which was diagonally across from the King's palace. 'It was a very busy corner of Oslo. At any hour of the day or night you could look out and see people coming and going.' The education of nurses has recently been made part of their general educational system. What they call their Institute of Nursing, which she visited, is very comparable to the Royal College of Nursing's Institute. One of its chief functions is conducting educational programmes. That Institute has been made part of the university system.

The day after she arrived, Virginia was the opening speaker at a seminar in a large convention centre. All the foreign visitors spoke that day: there was a great deal of emphasis on the function of the nurse in providing primary care but there was a range of subjects discussed.

The only thing that Virginia did other than go to these meetings for the three days that she was there was to go to the Institute. She met about thirty

Norwegian nurses there. They took time off to come and talk with her. One had written an article about Virginia and her work as a preliminary to her coming there. It was a very nice article, in Virginia's modest opinion.

In her address at the seminar, Virginia talked about the nursing process. Without regrets, she says, 'I think I was a little bit strong for the representative from California who made an address when I was not present. I gathered that he had expressed some reservations about some of the things that I had said.'

Virginia was made an honorary member of the Norwegian Nurses' Association at the meeting.

Spain

Virginia was also in 1987 invited to Spain for an extensive series of visits and lectures. She remembers that visit with fondness and is especially happy about the kindness and hospitality she received there. In fact, it was her second attempt to get there. The previous year, when she originally planned to go, the car taking her to the airport from her home in New Haven was involved in a serious crash. Virginia was so badly injured that she had to be admitted to hospital for lengthy treatment; but such is her abounding good health that she survived to return to Spain later.

Before going to Spain, it had been intimated that a Spanish university would award her an honorary doctorate. Unfortunately, that did not happen. Virginia's concern about that is not for herself but for Spanish nurses and nursing. She fears that the fact that the doctorate was not awarded may be illustrative of the lowly status of nurses and nursing in Spain. Nonetheless, she is more than delighted with the personal 'award' that the Spanish nurses gave her from their professional association.

Switzerland and France

Virginia has also been a guest speaker in Switzerland at an event which also attracted many nurses from Spain. There were various topics discussed at the meetings. She got the feeling that they were interested in new approaches. On one day she was taken to their hospital in Geneva, which had over a thousand beds, where she spent a lot of time with an experienced nurse who was in charge of the computer programme. She explained the computerised programme for patient records and the use that was made of it. Then she gave Virginia a thorough tour of the hospital. She told her that they now spent a fraction of their time on records since the use of the computer. This provides Virginia with an opportunity to state that 'It is frightening the amount of time spent on doing the records compared with the time spent on patients and, if the use of computers can transform that, it would be a very good thing.'

After that two-day meeting Virginia was driven to France by a French nurse and stopped in Lyons on the way to Paris to speak at a meeting there. They travelled by train from Lyons to Paris, where she had another speaking engagement to a capacity audience. She met a number of French nurses but was left with the distinct feeling that the French nurses have not managed to get away from the domination of physicians to the extent that they have in UK or in America. There was a reception after her speech but she was late for it because it seemed to her that every nurse in that audience came down afterwards with the ICN booklet for her to sign! Hence her late arrival at the reception.

She went on a marvellous shopping trip around Paris and visited Versailles where she had always wanted to go. She also went to the Left Bank for lunch and had a delightful time in an outdoor restaurant. The whole day was very memorable. On the visit to the American Hospital in Paris she met many more nurses.

Israel

In March 1985 Virginia was told that she had been awarded the ICN Christianne Reimann Award. She was amazed! In fact she had been asked to sit on the selection committee but had declined because she could not afford to attend frequently and did not think she could be a useful member if she could not go every time they met. In customary and true humility, Virginia comments thus about the award: 'I felt that people who were more actively engaged in nursing were much better judges of those people than I would be. It absolutely never entered my head that I would be named as the winner of that award. I still wish the awards were going to people who have demonstrated their ability to help people recover from disease and their handicaps'. She recalls her absolute amazement when she learnt that the prize was something like $30,000. She had a choice of taking it all or having her expenses to the ICN Quadrennial Congress in Israel deducted from the prize money. She chose the second because she wanted to go to that Congress: 'For nothing is more exciting to me than meeting nurses from all over the world and to discuss their common concerns.'

There were many pluses for Virginia connected with that trip, she says. She was very interested in what she saw of Israel but she was worried about the troubled state and the displacement of so many Arabs and was interested to learn as much as she could about how people coped in Israel. She admits she was treated in a very special way at the ICN Congress. There were pluses and minuses to this, she believes, because her time was so taken up with meeting groups so that she missed most of the sessions of the Congress. She regretted that. 'When I go to nursing meetings I don't go for the sideshows. I like to hear what is going on.' She did manage to get to the opening and closing sessions, otherwise she was meeting the press and small groups of people. Virginia was, however, able to meet one group of student nurses at a school of nursing in Tel Aviv, and she had a meeting with a group of student nurses who were at the ICN Congress. One evening the Japanese nurses made her an honorary member of their association at a marvellous dinner, which she appreciated very much.

Her reactions to the pilgrimage tour in Jerusalem, which she took after the Congress, are mixed. As she says, 'It seemed to me that the Way of the Cross had been completely industrialised. It was a money-making venture, rather than a reminder of the true event. It distressed me. I had a hard time with the guide who seemed to race through everything. I went to the church [of the Holy Sepulchre] that was in very bad repair and the paintings were covered in dust.' Neither was she cheered by the visit to Israel. It did not appear to her to be a happy country. When she went to Bethlehem she had to enter the Church of the Nativity through a tiny door because of security reasons. It just seemed distressing to her. She was also distressed by the relationship between Muslims and Jews and Christians, not least because she is still 'fearful of the Christian and Jewish Churches combining against the Muslim religion.' Virginia says she has never felt such a feeling of unhappiness that she detected in the State of Israel. No one smiled; everyone appeared to be glum. Sadly, 'It wasn't a moving religious experience. It was spoilt by the conditions.'

The political situation of the Arabs and the Jews affected her. 'Everywhere we went we saw soldiers in uniform', she recalls. 'I saw very little sign of friendliness between people. They try to keep alive the distress over the holocaust.' She had almost no contact with the Arab people while in Israel and regrets that, as she feels she ought to hear their side of the story, too.

When talking about the holocaust, Virginia concedes that it must be extremely difficult for Jewish people to forget about it. 'That is so like saying "Are the Southerners ever going to forget the Civil War?"' she says. She does not think she could forget these things but does not see any virtue in letting it dominate your life, your job and your feelings about people who had nothing to do with the terrible injury done. But, she adds, 'I suppose it is too recent for the Jewish people to forget it.' She has to admit that 'going to the museum illustrating the holocaust was so painful I will never forget it.'

Pakistan

Virginia also had a short trip to Pakistan in 1985 when she visited the School of Nursing at the Aga Khan University. She was invited for the first graduation of nursing students. She was also taken to a reception given by a Pakistani family and, as there was going to be a wedding there in two days' time, this was one of the prenuptial celebrations. All the women wore veils in front of the men, she recalls.

The nursing school was built around courts. The buildings were beautiful and designed by architects from all over the world. That university must be a marvel, in Virginia's view, because the barren ground around the building when she was there has now changed to greenery. I can confirm this as I was also fortunate to be able to visit that school of nursing myself in November 1985.

Virginia spent a number of days observing classes and meetings of the faculty at the school and got a good idea of the way they were functioning. She was taken on sightseeing trips. On one day she went out in a boat, fished and caught crabs, which were cooked on the stove aboard the boat.

She also took a day trip to a health centre and on her drive through the country she saw how arid the land was and how everything seemed to be the same colour. One had to look hard to see if there was any habitation in the land, she says. The health centre appeared to consist of mud huts, one of which was full of children brought by women. There were no qualified people, and only one person there to cope with the influx of patients. 'The treatment was basically back to grass roots', she says.

She was impressed with the concept of health of the Aga Khan and the people who worked with him who were extending the influence and resources of the big medical centre into the countryside. It was going to be a remarkable experiment with the co-ordination of hospital care and out-patient care. She discovered that the Aga Khan had been planning the health development in his country and had visited many countries to find out what was going on. He knew a fair amount about American practices. Virginia told him that the status of women in Pakistan would make it difficult for them as nurses because they would be prevented from doing so many things; the cultural restrictions were so great. She thought it would be a wonderful thing if he could encourage men to apply for entrance to the nursing school, and told him so. He disagreed with this. 'I am wondering whether medicine is reserved for men and nursing for women in that country', she ponders.

'The graduation ceremony was held in a vast tent and there was an enormous gathering. There were addresses from the Aga Khan and various dignitaries. The Aga Khan seems to be using his fortune very generously for the general good of Pakistan', Virginia recalls.

United Kindgom

Although Virginia Henderson had made personal trips to the United Kingdom before, her first 'official' visit was in 1977 when she was invited by the Association of Integrated and Degree Courses in Nursing (AIDCN) to deliver their annual Battersea Memorial Lecture in the Nightingale School of Nursing at St Thomas' Hospital, London. Christine Chapman was AIDCN chairman at that time (later to become Dean and Professor of Nursing Education at the University of Wales College of Medicine). Virginia also used the visit to speak at the University of Edinburgh, in Aberdeen, Scotland, and in Northern Ireland, and she also went to Wales.

Virginia vividly remembers visiting Northern Ireland because she was shocked at the treatment given to her at the airport 'because I was really searched'. It was the first time she had experienced that, but, she adds, she was treated with great courtesy. There was a reception at the RCN in Northern Ireland, which was delightful for her, and she visited many interesting places. She spoke in the evening to a large gathering in a hospital in Belfast.

During her visit to Scotland, in Edinburgh she addressed a large audience by candlelight during a blackout, which was a new experience for her! In Aberdeen she went to a school of nursing that had one of the finest libraries she has seen. A meeting with the Community Health Council was also arranged for her with representatives of all the health organisations in that community. It preceded the address that she was asked to make. In retrospect, Virginia feels that she 'said a good many things, I am sure, that were slightly disturbing to that group that were really doing such remarkable things in nursing, but I am afraid I gave them the feeling that it still was not good enough. This group was really outstanding in the progress it was making but I still said they were not making progress fast enough.'

It was in Aberdeen that she went to a health centre when, in her view, she really got the best picture of the way the health care system functioned. 'It was a large health centre', she recalls. 'There was a group of health visitors working at one end and district nurses at another, and also the doctors. I watched all these people functioning in relation to patients in a way that I had not been able to see anywhere else. I acquired great respect for it. The thing that I came away with that pleased me most was the humane attitude towards the patients that was typified by some worker coming down the hall and, seeing two elderly men waiting there, said to them in the sweetest way — as if it were their house — "Would you like a cup of tea?" And seeing the young woman bring them a cup of tea. You would never see anything as genuine and humane in any other setting.'

One thing that did trouble Virginia very much, because of her interest in health records, was that she found that the health visitors kept one set of records, the district nurses another and the doctors yet another set of records. As far as she could tell they made no effort to co-ordinate them. 'They disclaimed any common use. I felt — what a waste!'

Her general impression was of a very effective use of the National Health Service in Scotland, particularly the visiting nurse service that was available to people at night in emergencies. That was an outstanding development in her experience.

Her visit to Wales was short. A visit to a psychiatric hospital was arranged. In the hospital she was impressed by the fact that they had controlled the excited patients, but it seemed to Virginia that people were being subdued by drugs there to an unfortunate extent. This caused her to ponder on 'what we had been doing in past decades by putting psychiatric patients to work on large farms and giving them an occupation. Although it had nothing to do with any scientific approach to treatment, it at least occupied them and made them active physically.' She thought that those units in the Welsh hospital, with all the old people sitting around in chairs, was one of the gloomiest pictures that she has seen. She approved of things that she heard there but was not too impressed with what she saw, but says she may not have seen enough to form a fair opinion.

Another visit to England, in 1982, was to participate in a conference on critical care nursing. She was surprised at the invitation because she certainly did not consider herself an authority on that subject. Before she went to the conference she visited as many intensive care units as possible but she went to this conference not being sure what she could add to it. Nonetheless, her address was given a very warm welcome from the other participants. After the conference she was invited to see some of the work in the Brent Health Authority, London. She recalls, 'I was taken to a number of programmes in Brent. I was very impressed by the variety of institutions and agencies and I was impressed with the range of knowledge that the District Nursing Officer [the author] had to have to work with so many kinds of health agencies and health care providers. I was also impressed by the fact that he had managed to get so many of them to contribute to my visit, and so I got a feeling of how they were seeing their work and it was not just a view from the top. I felt that it gave me the best knowledge that I had had up to that time of the way the health care system operated in England. I had a pretty good sampling of the agencies serving a population of about 250,000.'

Virginia is a very great fan of the British National Health Service because it is a tax-supported health care system available to everybody, free at the point of delivery. The marked influence of the nurse on health care in Britain, as compared with the nursing influence in the USA, is recognised by historians and observers of all sorts, according to Virginia. A lot of American doctors are threatened by the experienced nurse who has been taking care of the old people for many years, she says, for 'he has all the knowledge in his mind but he has not learnt to use it.' Doctors in the USA are threatened by nursing, she believes, and they want — at least on paper — to limit the nurse's role. She feels in Great Britain that doctors do not feel threatened by nurses and, therefore, British nurses function up to their full potential without the friction that she feels has been imposed on American nurses by the medical profession.

Virginia came back to another British Nursing Conference in 1987, at which she had the formidable task of giving the final summation. It was for a conference to do with primary care to celebrate the hundredth anniversary of the Queen's Nursing Institute. It was, for her, an exciting meeting including many varied activities, like the special service at Westminster Abbey, which she thought was a beautiful ceremony. The Princess of Wales attended and Virginia was introduced to her.

As Virginia had been asked to summarise the conference, she thought the only way to do it honestly was to read the papers by some forty participants, or at least the summaries. So she spent a large part of the previous summer reading through the papers and 'it was one of the hardest tasks that I have ever had assigned to me to make the summary interesting.' It was, nonetheless, a masterly summation. I know: I was chairman of the session at which she spoke.

Virginia's reaction in November 1987 to the news that she was being created a life Vice-President of the Royal College of Nursing, is typical of Virginia Henderson's humility and joy: 'It was extremely flattering to me, on my ninetieth birthday, to receive from the Royal College of Nursing a bouquet of ninety red roses and with them came the news that I had been made a Vice-President of the College. I assumed that I would be an Honorary Vice-President, and it was only when I came to the RCN Fellows' meeting (in 1988) that I was informed I was mistaken and I was a Vice-President. I have been wondering ever since what a Vice-President should do!'

At Home

Virginia Henderson reached her ninetieth birthday on 30 November 1987 and was able to celebrate on that day with her own family and friends in New Haven, but the Yale University School of Nursing celebrated her birthday in a very special way on 8 April 1988.

On that day, Dean Judith Krauss, Dean of Yale University School of Nursing, welcomed a capacity audience to the University's auditorium who had come to celebrate Virginia Henderson's first ninety years. Guests came from all over North America and from Australia, France, Japan and the United Kingdom. Three keynote speakers were invited to record their and the nursing professions's tribute to Virginia.

Dr Susan Reverby, Director of the Women's Study Programme, Wellesley College, USA, said that Virginia Henderson represented the best of the past and the best of the future. Another speaker from the USA, Dr Edward Halloran, Director of Nursing, University Hospitals of Cleveland, focused on Virginia Henderson's attributes as a scientist and as a human being. She represented a mix of science, art and humanity, he said, but in her case 'they are lived traits'. The third speaker was from the United Kingdom. Trevor Clay, FRCN, said that he believed that Virginia Henderson was the first truly international nurse and the most important nursing voice since

Florence Nightingale. He said, 'She is quite unique: she has outlived all her competitors!'

Afterwards, Dr Virginia Henderson, RN, AM, FAAN, FRCN, Senior Research Associate Emeritus, Yale University School of Nursing, was given a standing ovation and later at a champagne reception was wished great happiness and many more years of activity.

Ad Multos Annos!

CHAPTER 13

What Friends Think about Virginia Henderson

Delia Henderson, School Nurse, Virginia Henderson's niece

I guess my youngest recollection of Virginia was when I was a child living in Richmond, Virginia, with my family and Virginia was always the exciting nurse who lived in New York. As a child, New York seemed like a million miles away because we only saw Virginia at Christmas time, and once in a while in the summer.

When my mother died, I was thirteen years old and I went to Trivium to live with my father's family. Virginia more or less became my mother (I guess she would say) because she put me through boarding school. I went to an Episcopalian boarding school in Virginia and she shared the expenses for that. She bought all of my clothes; so essentially she became my mother. But she was living in New York and it was always great fun for her to come home at Christmas or during the summer vacation, because she came laden with lovely clothes for me from Sachs, Fifth Avenue. At that point I hardly knew what Sachs, Fifth Avenue was.

I remember when I was a very young child and we would go to Trivium at Christmas or in the summer time, and it was such fun having Virginia there because she was always laughing. She loved children. She always played with me and we would have tea parties.

After boarding school, I went to college as a day student and, again, Virginia put me through college. As far back as I can remember I wanted to be a nurse and I am sure it was because of Virginia. When the time for me to apply to a nursing school there were two or three that we were thinking of. I think I really wanted to go to New York so that I would be near Virginia. She was living there then. I went up and saw Columbia Presbyterian and New York Cornell and decided that I would like to go to the Presbyterian Hospital, which I did. Virginia lived at 120th Street in New York. I recently went through a diary that I had kept and I seemed to have spent half my time at Virginia's apartment. I was either going down to Virginia's for dinner or I was going down to spend the night, and then we were going shopping the next day. Virginia took in my friends as well as myself, and they felt as if she was part of their family too. She was very very generous with her time, and food especially! To go down to dinner after having institutional food was wonderful.

There was always some sense of excitement when Virginia was around. When I finished nursing school I then worked at Columbia Presbyterian Hospital for three years before I married. Again Virginia was always around. My husband and I went to Boston to live in 1958 and our daughter, Catherine, was born in 1959; and of course Catherine was treated as the 'grandchild'. Virginia was always there whenever you needed her, whenever you were in trouble.

I can't remember that Virginia ever irritated me as a younger person. She never seemed to demand that I come to her apartment when I was living in New York. She always understood that I had other things to do and I think maybe I irritated her, because I wanted to come more often! I think that as I got older we have had many differences of opinion. I would state my opinion, and she would say, 'How can you think that?'

My daughter, Catherine, came to the Yale School of Nursing in 1982 and took the three-year programme for the Master's degree, and afterwards worked at the Yale New Haven Hospital for a good part of a year, and then went to the Connecticut Community Care Association where she is working now. So there are three generations of nurses in the family!

The whole family is so proud of Virginia. Catherine and I are very very proud, especially to be nurses ourselves. I think Virginia feels that the family does not appreciate her, but they do.

Catherine Mark, Public Health Nurse, Virginia Henderson's great-niece

The earliest memory that I have of Virginia was when she was in New York and we would go and visit her. Mother, father and I would go and stay in her apartment. Many times they would go out and leave me with her and sometimes they would go home and I would spend the night with Virginia. It was like a fantasy just to go into her apartment for a little child. She had all the toys and she had wonderful things to eat, and she made you feel very special. She was like my grandmother, especially as she was one of the most influential people in my mother's life, and was rather like a mother to her. I felt extremely close to her because she was not only my aunt but my 'grandmother' as well.

I remember she had a wooden doll that you could put a pipe into it and it would smoke. I shall never forget that once she burnt herself with a match and I was hysterical. It upset me so much that she had hurt herself; it didn't really bother her at all but it upset me to see her hurt. I do remember that she always tried to make everything very special. She had dolls there for me and there was always something to look forward to when Mum and Dad said they were going to see Virginia.

I don't think I knew how much Virginia was influencing me. I look back on it with interest, but it sure did work! The first thing that I remember about nursing was going to a capping ceremony at Columbia Presbyterian.

My mother, father and I were surprising Virginia. She was giving a lecture. She was really happy and I will never forget this ceremony and how mystical it all seemed. I also remember that she talked about me in this speech, which of course made me feel very special. It just shows how much she and my mother had influence on me.

In second grade at school we were asked to write about our three wishes. My first wish was to have a horse, and I had two, so that came true. The second wish was to be a good citizen, and the third was to be a nurse. Virginia told that story at the capping ceremony. As I grew up I wondered whether I wanted to go in the direction of nursing. However, I was with Virginia a lot. I would always be down with her in Virginia State. It is very hard to think of Virginia as a nurse, especially when she is with the family. She is just herself.

Virginia's relationships with her family are typical and normal. Everybody loves one other very very much and respects one other deep down very much but, of course, there are always little family squabbles. Everybody in my family has a very strong personality.

Virginia comes from a unique family of three sisters and four brothers. Out of the four sisters only one got married (and did not have any children) and all of them were professionals. At that time it was very unusual. Two were teachers, and Jane has been recognised at the school where she taught and a building has been named after her. Her other sister, Lucy, who was a teacher, was very much respected in her field; and then there is Virginia; and Frances who was very much respected as an executive assistant with the American Art Association in Washington. She did not get married until her thirties. They all had very strong and wonderful personalities and they all like to do things their own way, and sometimes there were clashes but they always resolved their arguments.

The family really likes to hear what is going on with Virginia. I think sometimes it is hard for her to understand her fate. With her at home or down in Virginia she is just like any other person and she is really special to me as my relative and as a friend, and she is not treated differently. I think sometimes the family has a hard time understanding the significance of her work, and think that is frustrating for her, because she really wants to share it with them. She does, and they do ask questions. But I think it is very hard to understand the problems of nursing, and even though it is a profession that affects everybody in life, I think sometimes it is difficult to express what you do and its significance, and the problems of nursing. We do have some great discussions at meal times!

The family definitely know that she has made a mark in the world and we are very proud of it, just as they are with everybody in the family. Everybody has left their mark in our family, but some have received more recognition than others.

There were more nurses on my mother's side and more doctors on my father's side. I was training to be a doctor but hated it at pre-med college and majored in art and history. Then I went to work at Sotheby's when I graduated from college. In New York City, the New York Hospital is a block away from Sotheby's and every day I would walk to work and I passed all the sick people outside, and would see the nurses going to work and I was always thinking that I wanted to be there, and didn't want to go to Sotheby's.

I didn't realise the nurses could get Master's degrees. I was really inspired by meeting some nurses and by their dedication, and their success in their field, and their perseverence in making nursing work. After that I talked about it with Virginia and she put me up with the Dean of the School of Nursing.

I think Virginia and I have different political views and a lot of our opinions may be based on politics. We have disagreements about the government not providing free health care. It is wonderful to have a person like Virginia to do that with! I am very reality-based and Virginia is very idealistic. I love to hear from her, though, and sometimes she can put me back on track, and you can but respect her for all that she has done.

When I first came to the Yale School of Nursing it was interesting to see how she was perceived. I knew that she was well-known and I knew her book. It was overwhelming to see how she was perceived and received. I kept it quiet at college that I was related to her because I wanted them to know me for who I am. When I graduated quite a few people still did not know. I must say at times it was hard when people did know who I was.

Everybody that I see with her has been so gracious and wonderful to her because they just appreciate what she has done for the profession. I think people really are in awe of her. I see her so much more as my relative than as a nursing celebrity, even though she has influenced me, and I know she is one. So it is very hard for me to understand what they are saying, and when I see her being treated the way she is, it sometimes puzzles me. Especially so at the beginning; now I really understand why she is being treated this way, and she deserves every bit of it though I still have trouble sometimes treating her that way.

I think she has definitely influenced me positively and I can't think of anything negative. She made me appreciate the arts, music, literature, travelling and culture. In nursing she taught me to inter-react with the patients and not to just look at them medically, but look at them as human beings. So she has influenced me both personally and professionally. Particularly professionally, because I always ask questions!

Marion Cleveland, formerly Director of Nursing, Columbia Presbyterian Medical Centre, New York City

I think I first met Virginia when I and a friend went to Teacher's College to get a degree and she was my teacher. We had a wonderful time at the college and Virginia's influence was evident. We became friends and her influence in everything was felt. She is artistic and she helped us in renovating our house. She has an architectural sense and, more recently, she helped a great deal in making our country house into a beautiful home for us.

We also had what we called the 'Cabinet'; that was because five of us were very good friends and every now and then we would get together and we handled difficult questions that bothered us. That has gone on for years and we still say, 'Well, when the cabinet gets together we will sort things out.'

I think Virginia always had rather a liberal point of view politically and in education, too. I think I grew to feel that way, too.

Thomas Alm, final year graduate nursing student, Yale University School of Nursing, New Haven

I had the pleasure of meeting Miss Henderson for the first time in the fall of 1986 at my clinical professor's home. She invited Miss Henderson on the occasion of her eighty-ninth birthday and for a sort of pre-Christmas celebration. It was just wonderful to meet her. There were about fifteen students gathered, and she just came into the room and lit up the room, and we enjoyed supper together and an evening of conversation about anything.

Miss Henderson spoke about nursing, medicine, the state of health care in the USA and internationally in all the various countries that she has visited. She recited her definition of nursing for us. That was priceless and incredible!

There have been a few other occasions when she has come to the school for various research seminars. Her sense of humour is just incredible and she is such a warm person. I have had so many pleasurable moments visiting with her and also reading her works.

Kay Flynn, Associate Professor, Yale University School of Nursing

When I first met Virginia in the 1960s I was a young faculty person in a school of nursing. She hung up a board in the office with her definition of nursing on it: 'The unique function of a nurse is to assist the person that is sick or well in performance of those activities that he could do for himself, if he had the strength and will and knowledge.' I thought it was absolutely beautiful.

In the late '60s I returned to Boston College and one day there was a notice in the college saying that Virginia Henderson was going to speak at Boston College. I went to that event the evening she came and I can remember that she came in a long gown and she commented on her dress because in the late 1960s mini skirts were very popular. I think I came to know her through that event from many points of view. One is that she

111

often opened up a presentation by poking fun at herself or commenting to relax both herself and the audience, and it also always endeared the audience to her because one got to know something about her person — which was not common with most presenters. On that evening she talked about her definition of nursing and how she had arrived at her definition.

Her interest in nurses and nursing continues to amaze people. Her awareness of the things of life, the beauty with which she surrounds herself in her home and the gracious manner with which she greets people makes one sometimes lost for words to describe her. She has a wonderful sense of humour.

It has seemed to me over the years that the focus of the nursing curriculum was to prepare people for practice. I therefore used her work. I continue to quote her definition of nursing in working with students because I think her three words: the *strength, will* and *knowledge* apply over and over again in the practice setting.

Another thing about Virginia is that she often says that American nurses did not use her work or know her work, but I have not been at a nursing conference in the past five years where someone doesn't quote her definition of nursing and attribute that definition to her. I have also seen the definition used without identifying the author but I think that is because it has become so well-known and so commonplace that people don't realise that it had a time and an origin!

Eleanor Herman, Associate Professor, University of Connecticut School of Nursing

I was previously on the faculty of Yale University School of Nursing and that is when I met Virginia, in about 1976. Since then we have had numerous contacts. She has been a dear friend, a colleague, a supporter, and has always been a strong advocate of nursing.

One of the things that always struck me about Virginia is that she has the ability to delightfully blend the practical with the aesthetic. Let me give you an example: if we have a heavy snowfall here in New Haven it is highly unlikely that it will stop Virginia from going anywhere, because she is always on the go. When there is snow or icy conditions it would be very typical to see her walking along with a single ski pole in her hand — the tip of it digging into the ice to avoid her falling. That is one example of her practicality. Another is the fact that she makes many of her own clothes but, if she doesn't make them, she does many alterations to suit her particular personality. She is very conscious about the combination of colours and the presentation of her clothes.

To give a couple of examples of the aesthetics: you don't go to a party at Virginia Henderson's house without having a tray of sweetmeats and the sweetmeats are lovely candies or cookies that she has made, and always, always very much chocolate there. Typical would be pieces of candied

112

ginger dipped in chocolate or pretzels, or home-made truffles. A lovely assortment and beautifully arranged on a tray. Another example is that if you were to receive a gift from Virginia Henderson you can be quite sure that the package would be as elegant as the choice that she has made to put inside the package.

There is always a sense when she is in your presence of her tremendous pride in the nursing profession; recognising that the profession of nursing still has to move ahead in things that it needs to do — for that is part of its development — as opposed to looking at the profession in a negative fashion. That is not to say that she is not critical of some of the things that we have done in nursing. However, when you are with her you just know that there is a tremendous pride in the heritage of nursing and in the profession as a whole.

On quite a few occasions I have had Virginia as a guest speaker in some of my classes, but she never had to prepare for class! No previous preparation was necessary, of course, because Virginia was always well-prepared just from her own knowledge base. She often brought in some little known facts about nursing simply because of her own association in the past with a variety of rather influential groups.

It was not unusual for Virginia to be rather self-effacing when it came to describing her own accomplishments. She would usually make some kind of joke about it but, in reality, I am quite sure she is very much aware of her part in history.

Of course, in my estimation the major contribution which she has made to nursing has been the *Nursing Index*. As a student of the 1950s, I did not have such an *Index* available to me so I am particularly aware of the tremendous contribution that it made to our being able to move ahead in the profession in a scholarly manner. The *Index* was an incredible undertaking.

In a group, Virginia does not usually seek to have the attention brought on to her. She is the kind of person who turns around and will make sure that other people are included in the conversation. She is very much aware of the presence of other people and their contributions.

My husband is an attorney and is the kind of person who will be polite in any situation but he is more than that to Virginia; what Virginia has really done is charm my husband. He dearly loves her and recognises the contribution she has made as a human being as well as a nurse. He has also recognised the influence that she has had on my life and is quite grateful for that.

Something that has always kind of concerned me is that in the United States we always look to Florence Nightingale as the founder of modern nursing, even though we certainly have many other major leaders in nursing and among them are some very fine Americans. I would add though that I think that if we were to select the American Florence Nightingale, Virginia Henderson would be one of the final contenders, and one of the top contenders for such a position.

Florence Wald, former Dean (1958–68), Yale University School of Nursing

During the time I was Dean I had my office adjacent to Virginia Henderson's when she was working on the *Index of Nursing Studies*. My problem at that stage was that I was quite young and never thought of myself as a nurse educator in terms of its administration, but I assimilated ideas from Virginia who spoke in terms that I was very comfortable with — the fact that there was not enough research on the practice of nursing and that was the central theme that we were all involved with.

The other gift that I received from Virginia was her deep, broad knowledge, and her scholarship. It was essentially as if she were acting as my tutor. She has always been very beloved by all at the school of nursing. I think that the opening words of Annie Goodrich's book describe her experience exactly: 'Her generosity and her *joie de vivre* in anything which she undertook was infectious and inspirational'.

Our children and grandchildren are devoted to Virginia and whenever possible she is included in our holiday celebrations and birthdays; when she is a guest at our table for our Sunday brunches, the conversation is inevitably vigorous and full of laughter but also very attentive to issues that might be controversial. Virginia is always keeping up to date on nursing or health care but very frequently on other topics as well.

In reviewing what she has written over the years, Virginia has been a guide to me in her marvellous vocabulary, and her sense of structure and her phrases are always crystal-clear and unaffected.

During the time that I was developing a hospice in New Haven, Virginia was a very powerful force on the task force for in-patient planning. While this was an interdisciplinary group, Virginia's contribution was exceptional: her interest in colours, art, architecture, decoration, choice of furniture, planning of the food service and Child Care Centre were things that she took a great delight in. Virginia and our talented architect, Louis Chan, developed a wonderfully collaborative and fruitful relationship.

The saying around the Yale School of Nursing is that everyone wants to grow old the way Virginia Henderson does, and certainly she has influenced my whole development as a senior citizen. While I often worry at the enormous amount of work and energy and the friendships and relationships with the family, I worry that Virginia is spending too much of her energy and not leaving enough time for herself. Surely the way she acts and feels, her mind and body are not that of a ninety-year-old. In fact, one feels that in the last four or five years if anything she has grown younger!

Tom Cook, Home Care Nursing Co-ordinator, Vanderbilt Hospital, Nashville, Tennessee

I met Virginia Henderson in 1981 when I first came on the faculty at the

Yale School of Nursing. I had been in nursing for approximately twenty years at that time. I had learned Virginia's definition of nursing as a student and had mixed feelings about it. Mostly these feelings were positive but it was after meeting Virginia and listening to her that I more completely understood the definition. The personality of Virginia Henderson adds a lot to the understanding of her definition of nursing. My other thoughts about Virginia are gentleness, kindness and thoughtfulness, the detail of the things which she remembers about people and the concern that she has to see nursing quickly moved forward.

One of my opportunities as a nurse was to be able to provide nursing service as a nurse practitioner to Virginia when she was ill. She was in an automobile accident in 1982 and injured her back. She was very uncomfortable. As she was a member of the insurance plan where I was working she came to see me. I had the opportunity of carefully assessing her complaints and of providing actual care for her, for which she has always been most grateful.

Ruth Gardner, former schoolteacher, New Haven

I have lived with Virginia Henderson for the last fourteen years, sharing the apartment at 164 Linden Street. I first knew Virginia when I lived above her at 162 Bishop's Street and when we both had to find new apartments I looked around everywhere for one for myself, and found a small one here in the Claremont Apartments. They said they had a much nicer one up on the 3rd floor at 164 Linden Street and so I came and looked at it and decided that it was very charming but it was too big for me and too expensive for me alone. I asked Virginia if she would consider sharing it with me and she said that she would be delighted and that she didn't have to think about it. So for fourteen years we have shared this apartment.

Virginia is a very unusual person. I know her only in a domestic way; I know nothing about nursing. Virginia is very skilful with her hands and it was she who did most of the planning and decorating of the apartment. The fireplace distressed her because it was very ugly in its appearance so she designed a new frame for it and had a painter and carpenter come and make it as she wanted it. She had the floors stained with a dark stain instead of the usual light stain. She had the base boards painted black. She chose the colours for the room. I feel really the charm of the apartment is largely due to her artistic ability.

She is very skilful with her hands in all ways. She sews beautifully and makes nearly all her own clothes. She finds it difficult to get anything to fit her in the stores but she can buy something and then make it over so that it will fit her. She also makes things from the start. She loves materials. She has a pile of materials that she has gathered together in one of her cupboards that looks almost like a dry goods store. She likes buying dresses at thrift shops if they have lovely material in them and then uses the material. She is very good at making things. She loves to make boxes. She takes boxes and covers them in beautiful materials and pastes beautiful pictures on top, and sometimes she decorates them with velvet ribbon or gilt braid, and before she puts anything in them she must have beautiful ribbons to tie them all up with; nothing is just plain with Virginia, everything is beautifully decorated.

Virginia has very definite opinions and she always says 'in my opinion', and she loves to tell the story that she thinks should be engraved on her tomb stone: 'In my opinion Virginia Henderson lies here.' She likes lots of everything around her. She has a collection of small boxes in her room — hundreds. They are on her dressing table, on the bureau, on a tiny bookcase on her wall. She likes to be surrounded by lots of things in the kitchen; lots of food and she must always have the ice box well-stocked: it gives her a feeling of security, she says.

Virginia loves colour, especially if it is pink, and she has a great idea of symmetry. Everything must balance. If there is a little dish on one end of the table, there must be a similar dish on the other end of the table. She is distressed by the lack of symmetry in the yard at the back of the apartment.

She has a remarkable memory. Everything she has ever read she can remember and quote and she reads very largely all kinds of books. She has a great interest in people because of her interest in all humanity. Surprisingly, she has a great interest in television personalities, and one would indeed be surprised to know that she spends so much time looking at television. In the morning, she likes to look at a particular show from 9 a.m. to 10 a.m. She is interested in all the people that the presenter brings to the show and she thinks that he is a great person himself. She is interested even in a soap opera because she says she likes the people in it. She wants to know what they are doing.

Virginia has a unique personality and everyone remembers her. Even the clerks in stores, the taxi drivers; the bag man who stands outside and calls her 'Miss Marples'. She has amazing hospitality and wants to entertain and, indeed, does entertain everyone who comes near her very well. She loves to shop both in stores and in catalogues and she has the apartment cabinets full of gifts that are always ready if she wants to give a gift to somebody. She wants to give a gift to somebody most of the time. She even tells stories on herself that at one time when she was approaching a house where two of her relatives were looking out of the window, one of them said to the other 'Here comes Virginia and her damn presents!' She is always ready with the presents. They are always beautifully done up, and I am sure very much appreciated by everybody.

Virginia is a remarkable person and I think that I have been privileged to live with her these years.

Index

117